WHY NATURE CONSERVATION ISN'T WORKING

UNDERSTANDING WILDLIFE IN THE MODERN WORLD

Adrian Spalding

Foreword by Kurt Jackson

ISBN 978-1-8381528-4-0

Published by Siri Scientific Press, Manchester, UK

This and related titles are available directly from the publisher at:

https://www.siriscientificpress.co.uk

Dedication

This book is dedicated to my children Dylan, Josie, Trystan

and Taran Mark, and to the memory of Jack.

CONTENTS

Acknowledgements

I wish to acknowledge the help and support of all the friends

and colleagues mentioned in the book.

FOREWORD
by Kurt Jackson

Recently I completed a new body of work, 'Biodiversity' aiming to engage with the spectrum of wildlife found in the UK, exploring the differences between various locations and habitats and to look at that vast array of animals and plants living in this country; a series of paintings, drawings and sculpture.

My artistic practice takes me outdoors to work with nature directly, on the ground as it were, and these direct experiences are what feed my creativity. It is an engagement but also a collaboration because if allowed both the wildlife and the elements will become involved, steer the art, make their own marks. The outdoors, in situ, is where I make my discoveries, explore and hopefully, ultimately make breakthroughs. It is the dynamic side of plein air painting – the excitement resulting from allowing nature to surround me, collide and collude, interrupt or visit that provides the excitement, the sparkle to a painting session, making it all worthwhile. It can be hard work, unsuccessful but often also memorable and remarkable. My quietness, my absorption and concentration, usually alone, allows me an invaluable window into the natural world. To have a bird perch upon you, to sing next to you or to stare into a kestrel's eye as it drops onto a field mouse that had also looked you in the eye. To have a weasel, a stoat, shrews, voles, adders, lizards all pass by within touching distance or have dragonflies, butterflies, hoverflies alight upon you or on the painting. To have the sea, the wind, the sunlight, lightning, leaf fall, rainfall add their own signatures to the work. The seasons shift, migrants arrive and depart, courtship, breeding, hatching, flowering, fruiting all occurs around me; it is noted, documented, described. These are my ingredients just as much as the individual pigments and media all add up to the final work.

Anything can happen. Deer come crashing into my space, sparrowhawks chase swallows, bats, finches across my page. Bugs, beetles, bees trudge through and across my wet paint, seals stare at me just offshore, dolphins keep me company, salmon leap to land at my feet, eels swim slowly past me. Sometimes I am only witness to a snatch of birdsong, the lingering scent of a fox, the slots of deer tracks in the mud, an individual wildflower in blossom but this is enough to make that session, that place and the painting about that creature or plant. A redshank calls across an estuary, that estuary then becomes the redshank's as does the painting.

The narrative and the experience of making the art is vital; it is subject and content and the context; it is not just the final work alone that is important.

What I am noticing during these active painting times is the life around me, the plants and animals I share this place with; above, below, around me; sometimes subtle, sometimes bold and in your face – the minutiae and the macro but also I notice how the abundance or paucity will vary from site to site. I'm excited by the variety of life to be seen and found, the richness of diversity and how they slot into their niches and habitats, how they relate to each other, are dependent on each other, stack up into their web and chains. But what also goes hand in hand with this fascination are the concerns and worries that come with the awareness of the frequent lack and loss of biodiversity, that blandness and emptiness that exists in some places and then the small size of some populations, the lack of viability with some species. My passion is accompanied by worry. A location may be an amazing biodiverse hotspot but with a lack of biomass – there may be a dozen species of birds of prey to be seen but only one or two of each. Five or six species of fritillary butterfly but very few individuals.

I paint these places and their animal and plant communities, I note what I see or find but most of life is invisible to us and therefore is missed by my brush and pencil. The fungi, the bacteria, algae, the lichen and mosses, the small invertebrates. By remaining hidden they often elude our thoughts when in fact they are the fundamental ingredients of this world, the support system, the building blocks. For example we read that our soils are in decline in quality [and quantity] but we don't see it, maybe it feels to be out of our hands, too massive a problem, the scale, the magnitude.
What can **we** do?

Attenborough has suggested that we all spend 10 minutes daily allowing nature to reveal herself, to sit quietly outside and observe. I spend my life doing this; solitary, observing, making my marks. It is worthwhile and does change your mindset; but if the wildlife is not there to be seen any more or is elusive or rare then it will be missed or irrelevant. It usually needs patience, maybe guidance and even help.

I have always argued that we need to be aware of what we share this place with to appreciate it and then hopefully conserve it.
But the conserving bit…. where do we come into that?

We can all make choices and changes.
Our diets [climatavore, flexitarian, ethical omnivore, vegetarian, vegan, organic] our life styles, how we live – all has an impact on the planet and therefore the wildlife. We are consumers and producers simply by living.

Do we cut the lawn, do we leave it, do we only cut it seasonally, do we use an electric mower, petrol or a push and pull? Do we even have a lawn or do we let it go to scrub; do we plant it with trees instead; do we even own, rent or use land? There are so many decisions, let alone those about using chemicals: the moss killers and dandelion removers. Do we choose the pollinators, the nesting birds or our own mental wellbeing or can we have it all?

Artists are often said to ask the questions rather than give the answers or find the solutions. But art can help make science become more accessible; more approachable, less academic, more attractive, I believe in breaking down boundaries, removing the pigeonholing but not dumbing down. We need to all be involved in the future of our environment and wildlife; aware, observant, commenting, changing, adapting – life needs to be a mosaic of approaches and attitudes just as the natural world requires a mosaic of habitats and topography to be healthy.

Outside
And we went back to Scilly
And after a big evening meal with lots of wine and curry
Richard showed us a film on his big TV
In the front room
About the South West coast
Which was very beautiful
But outside 10 feet away
In the late low sunshine
With oystercatchers calling
And plover chicks running around
And wind in the thrift
Was the real thing
And then when we got home
Late, the next evening
We sat and watched a film
And a white moth beat against the window only to remind us again of the real world
Outside.

6/06

Kurt Jackson is a contemporary artist, a dedicated environmentalist and a true polymath. Jackson's artistic practice ranges from his trademark visceral plein-air sessions to studio work and embraces an extensive range of materials and techniques including mixed media, large canvases, print-making, sculpture and the written word. Over the past thirty years Jackson has had numerous art publications released to accompany his exhibitions. Five monographs on Jackson have been published by Lund Humphries depicting his career so far; *A New Genre of Landscape Painting* (2010), *Sketchbooks* (2012), *A Kurt Jackson Bestiary* (2015), *Kurt Jackson's Botanical Landscape* (2019) and *Kurt Jackson's Sea* (2021). A new publication, *Biodiversity* to accompany the touring exhibition Biodiversity was published in 2021. Kurt Jackson and his wife Caroline live and work in the most-westerly town in Britain, St Just-in-Penwith where in 2015 they set up the Jackson Foundation. www.kurtjackson.com

INTRODUCTION

The butterfly flapping against a window is not the same as a butterfly flapping in its own habitat. It is about context[1]. This book attempts to put species (plants and animals) into the context of our perception, in their historical setting; it discusses the movement of species since the last ice age, what is native and non-native, migration, adaptation, the role of man and species in the industrial landscape. It is not a book about habitats[2] or nature conservation, so some might consider it old fashioned – but I have learned over many years that habitats are made up of species, and conservation is more successful when targeted at key species than when focussed on broad habitats.[3] The key modern threat to wildlife from human-induced climate change can only be understood in the species context. The concept of species lies at the heart of nature conservation, and our perception, which I discuss from a western European English perspective, is changing and perhaps losing connection with a world beyond the limited horizons of our garden windows or our organised tropical rainforest adventures. We need to recognise the different ways people can view wildlife and be aware of these alternative views in deciding where we want to go in the future. I also emphasise the importance of individual species and in doing so I wish people to recognise the value of history and wildness and the separateness of wildlife, but within the context of our modern crowded industrial environment, where we can celebrate the way wildness invades our space. Like Jay Griffiths in her 2008 book *Wild: An Elemental Journey*, I am "looking for a quality of wildness, which, like art, sex, love and all the other intoxicants, has a rising swing ringing through it."

This book investigates different ways of seeing wildlife. We cannot see wildlife as separate from our understanding of the world. We no longer see wildlife as wild or independent from us, but as adjuncts of people. So in covid-19 times we see wildlife just as a cure for depression and isolation. With this view, we will never save wildlife from extinction. In this book I look closely at animals and plants in the context of their individuality, their history and geography. Animals are more than their physical form. They exist within their historical setting, within their habitats, within their past and their evolutionary future, both outside and beyond man, and within man and his circle, within their individual movements. The book looks at where animals and plants come from, how they arrived here, how we use – and abuse – them, how we get excited by them, how they survive now in the

---

1. The same can be considered for wines. You can just drink the wine or you can consider its "terroir" or character, context and authenticity - how a particular region's climate, soils and aspect (terrain) affect the taste of wine. It would be a great shame to down a glass of Chateau D'Yquem without enjoying its terroir.

2. We now have to consider biodiversity net gain when assessing planning developments; at the time of writing this gain is entirely based on habitats not on species. The pre and post-development habitats are assessed according to habitat distinctiveness, condition (actual and anticipated), ecological connectivity and strategic significance and (for created habitats) time to target condition and difficulty of creation. There is currently (spring 2021) a move to include species which could be a welcome step forward.

3. An excellent example is the project for the re-establishment of the Large Blue butterfly – see later.

industrial urbanised landscape – and how they adapt and survive after Man has retreated (e.g. at Chernobyl and during pandemics). I emphasise that wild animals see things differently – their wildness is an essential part of their existence and our modern life is an existential threat to their survival.

So in this book I am attempting to investigate the authenticity of species, compared with what I term McDonald's species – species without natural connection with their habitats, species super-imposed by Man on existing or newly created habitats, eroding the umbilical cord connection with history, the equivalent of drinking a fizzy drink rather than eating a heathy balanced diet.

I hope that this book is relevant to current thinking on the value of nature to humankind and national strategies on access to the countryside and our relationship to wildlife. It is about wildness versus tameness, naturalness versus artificiality; it points out the difference between pets and wild animals. It is not a book directly about nature conservation – which is our attempt to mitigate the damage we do to the environment – but about our view of wildlife from the safety of our homes in front of the television screen, from the offices of council planners, from the nature conservation charities. Without a fuller understanding of wildlife many of our attempts at nature conservation will fail. We are failing now – even though wildlife charities get larger and more powerful, more species are legally protected, more species are listed as Priority Species for planning purposes, more emphasis is placed on Biodiversity Net Gain in planning policies, more people watch nature programmes on television. We have lost sight of what wildlife is about. Without this understanding we cannot fully understand wildlife and cannot manage our countryside. We are just managing decline – wildlife reserves are managing slow retreat – *State of Nature* reports show that we are losing species but spending more money than ever and building larger conservation empires. Conservation success is now based on getting people involved and on access to nature – and species abundance declines and species become extinct.

Mace (2014) has suggested that conservation thinking can be divided into four stages: Nature for Itself (before the 1960s), Nature despite People (in the 1970s and 1980s), Nature for People (late 1990s) and now People and Nature. These stages reflect changes in our perception of the role of wildlife in the modern world, and conservation thinking has moved away from species and toward ecosystems as a focus for integrated management, managing nature to maximize the overall value for the human condition. However, in practice it represents a superficiality of understanding of wildlife and a proud emphasis on the superiority of humans. People and Nature is meant to recognise a two way, dynamic relationship and the importance of developing sustainable and resilient interactions between human societies and the natural environment, but it is one sided; it fails as it places people first in all cases, it mis-represents species, does not recognise them for what they are as individuals, mis-understands how they fit into the natural world and shows no understanding of the complexities of our perceptions.

Good intentions, quick fixes, cosy books and colourful tv programmes are fine, but get us nowhere. Concentration on large iconic species achieves brilliant publicity but looks after the icing whilst the cake crumbles beneath.

This book does not aim to go back to a mythical wonderful time in the past. It highlights the need for authenticity in wildlife, where plants and animals can survive not just where they have occurred over centuries but where they have naturally colonised new habitat, by migration and by evolution. It uses examples from the art world where artists have tried to see the environment from the animal's point of view. It is a new way of looking at wildlife where we accept where wildlife goes, minimising our interference, re-directing money towards where wildlife wants to be – in new as well as old habitat, by natural colonisation, in post-industrial landscapes, brown-field sites, railway corridors, metal-contaminated landscapes. It takes rewilding and makes it species led – not for Man, not for our recreation, enjoyment and health, not as a green gym, but plant and animal (even insect) led; where ugly animals thrive as well as beautiful ones, where minute creatures are as important as huge ones.

Note
English names for species are used throughout where they are universally recognised. For completeness, the scientific names for these species are listed in the index after the English names.

CHAPTER 1: THE EXISTENTIAL SPECIES

Species are widely regarded by biologists as the primary units of biodiversity and conservation (Wilson 1992) and the natural taxonomic rank to form the basis for both conservation assessments and for management (Mace 2004). We can view them in different ways: as "other"/alien; as within our possession/ownership (as our possession increases over time it can reduce the wholeness, independence and integrity of animals); as an extension of ourselves; as representing aspects of our psyche and civilization. We can also view them from an existentialist point, investigating the authenticity of species within their own viewpoint, not a superimposed anthropomorphological standpoint, each individual species having a certain amount of freedom to act within its physical and historical environment.[4] Sartre (1945) suggested that humans were apart from non-human animals which mostly follow the instincts and behaviours that characterise their species, and that "Man can create his own definitions (or nature, or essence) in a way that never happens with other life forms. I create myself constantly through action", but in fact of course even humans are restricted by their environment. As a corollary, animals have some freedom of action and individuality. In an interesting paper published in 2015, Tuf, Drábková & Šipoš found that the Common Rough Woodlouse showed individual personality traits (independent of body size) by showing different individual responses to being touched, squeezed and dropped, with differences between some consistently more "bold" woodlice and some more "shy" woodlice. The recognition that even invertebrates have personalities at once makes them both more like people and more alien as they show independent response.

So in this book I attempt to investigate the authenticity of species within their own existence, each with a certain amount of freedom to act within their physical and historical environment. I look at species within their authentic habitats. John Ruskin (1856) coined the term *pathetic fallacy* to describe the assignment of human feelings to inanimate objects such as the sea (*the cruel seas*) and wild species such as daffodils (*tossing their heads in sprightly dance*). The personification of wildlife is one of the major viewpoints of the modern urban citizen, and is perhaps increasing as distance from actual wildlife habitat increases. Lucia Chmurova from Butterfly Conservation told me at the 2019 National Moth Conference that in her native Slovenia there was almost no one working on wildlife but she could watch wolves and bears just outside her house, whereas in the UK there were thousands of people working for wildlife but almost no wildlife! There appears to be an inverse correlation between the numbers of conservation workers and the amount of wildlife.

---

4. In Sartre's 1938 novel *Nausea*, Roquentin looks at the boiled leather of a chestnut tree and realises that it is not just the tree but the Being of the tree that bothers him. It simply sits there refusing to make sense or tone itself down. "I slumped on the bench, dazed, stunned by that profusion of beings without origin: blooming, blossoming everywhere, my ears were buzzing with existence, my very flesh was throbbing and opening, abandoning itself to the universal burgeoning."

Other/alien

It has been suggested that cultural severance between people and animals started with industrialisation (Rotherham 2014). He defined cultural severance as "best considered as the end of traditional, local, and often subsistence management and the results are predictable, long-term ecological successions with associated increases in available nutrients and biomass, and rapid declines in biodiversity." This led to a separation between people and wildlife and he suggests that this separation is wrong on many levels (social, ethical, economic and political) and that there is a belief that if we can only remove people from the landscape, ecology will thrive. This belief is based on a view of wildlife as alien, surviving best away from Man. Later in this book (Chapter 7), I attempt to show that this is a narrow, limited viewpoint, but we may still see species as different to us, unknown and not understood. From the animal's point of view, "No animal confirms man, either positively or negatively .... Always its lack of common language, its silence, guarantees its distance, its distinctiveness, its exclusion, from and of man" (Berger 2009).

Berger (2009) also suggests that animals were a key part of man's existence in the past, but in "the last two centuries, animals have gradually disappeared. Today we live without them." This may have been true in 1977 but it is not now. We are surrounded by images of animals in the media, on television and in nature writing, and exotic pets such as tarantulas and bearded dragons are common. *The Blue Planet*[5] and Gordon Buchanan bring wildlife into our houses so we feel we know about Snow Leopards and Blue Whales – but the wildlife remains on the other side of our television screens, or in our pet cages, and remains alien to us. This is not just an urban perspective. Residents in their country cottages walk their dogs in the local woodland and across the fields, but may not see the wildlife there. Many a time when doing bat surveys we come across householders who say "I've lived here in the country for thirty years and never seen a bat", only for us to find large colonies flying in and out of the roof above their heads on warm still summer nights.

The artist Marcus Coates expresses it well: Animals "aren't a version of us, they're their own species, autonomous beings, so to call an animal by a name is quite an odd thing. To see their behaviour as part of our own behaviour is not realising the specialities of the animal itself." Quite a lot of his work is about attempting to become an animal. In 2009 he wore a badger on his head and offered shamanic advice[6] in an Israeli shopping centre; after half an hour there was a queue of people waiting to ask him questions. He tries to understand animals from their point of view, so in his 1999 work *Goshawk* he was suspended in a pine tree so that he might view the world as a bird of prey, in *Sparrow Hawk Bait* (1999) he ran through a wood with his head covered in dead birds and in *Indigenous British*

5. Presented by David Attenborough.
6. A shaman would attempt to become an animal or non-human which may be linked to the animal world and may wear regalia, some part of which usually imitates an animal – most often a deer, a bird, or a bear (Encyclopaedia Britannica https://www.britannica.com/topic/shamanism).

Mammals (2000) he was partially buried in wild moorland, performing a karaoke of bird songs. There is a lovely photo of him (2004)[7] wearing a deerskin with a full set of antlers whilst a small woman looks at him in amazement holding firmly onto her shopping trolley. Another of his major works – *Dawn Chorus* – was a multi-channel 14 screen video installation showing people re-creating the dawn chorus of male birds defending their territories and attracting mates. Marcus is interested in the crossover of inter-species boundaries and finds birds especially interesting because their lives mirror our own (e.g. in nest building as homes and complex communicating rituals). He persuaded a Chelsea supporter to sing abusive chants threatening violence because this is what the birds are doing in their battle for survival. He says quite rightly "We hear a beautiful sound and imagine it a reflection in nature of our best parts ….. But when you study birdsong there's a lot of proxy violence." His interest in 'becoming animal' continued in a series of self-portraits from 2013 in which he transformed himself into a range of insects and molluscs by encasing his body in shaving foam, cotton wool, sugar and flour paste producing pale photographic images of an Iron Prominent moth larva (self-portrait, shaving foam), a Common Slug (self-portrait cottonwool), a standing Convolvulus Hawk-moth (self-portrait, shaving foam), a Fox Moth on all fours (self-portrait, shaving foam) and a Comma Butterfly larva (self-portrait in sugar).[8] None of these images resemble in any way the named invertebrates, which perhaps adds emphasis to the alien nature of these species.

Alienation also relates to the separate nature of individuals. This is a complex philosophical concept beyond the scope of this book as some species exist as clones, other individuals change within their life cycle (e.g. butterfly metamorphosis), yet other individuals survive in some form by regrowth (e.g. plant cuttings) (see for example Wilson & Barker 2013) but relevant to this book in the sense that alienation is in some sense an individual concept. An individual organism may be defined as a living thing that exists on its own and suffers only one death, which has functional autonomy and continuity of form, e.g. a tree starts when the seed germinates (Farjon 2015) and a clone becomes an individual when it becomes detached from the larger clone. The two key attributes are continuity of form and connectivity of parts (Farjon 2015). Identical twins are separate individuals as I know myself having a twin brother; each twin may have remarkably different life styles, preferences, longevity and career success.

Some forms of life are more alien to us than others, of course. The Ugly Animal Preservation Society was established in 2012 by Simon Watt to raise the profile of some of nature's more aesthetically challenged creatures; the plight of the panda is known the world over because of its teddy-like good looks, but most species are not so lucky. "It is time to celebrate the Ugly Animals."[9] Insects may be considered as wilder than mammals and birds because they can't be tamed and cannot answer to their names. The reasoning may be irrational. For example, bees are loved whilst

7. https://www.workplacegallery.co.uk/artists/9-marcus-coates/works/
8. http://visualarts.britishcouncil.org/collection/artists/coates-marcus-1968/objects/all/initial/a
9. https://www.uglyanimalsoc.com/

wasps are hated (Sumner, Law & Cini 2018), despite wasps having a valuable function in the regulation of crop pests and insect vectors of human disease; even academic researchers prefer bees. Words used to describe wasps are emotive and negative, whilst words describing bees are functional and positive. The European Wasp is considered by Australians as a dangerous animal.

Simon Leather has introduced two new words into language:[10]

- *Entomyopia* – entomological short-sightedness; a condition in which insects are viewed either as pollinators or as nuisances; a lack of foresight or discernment as to the importance of entomology: a narrow view of entomology.

- *Entoalexia* – entomological blindness; a condition in which a person or organisation is totally oblivious to the importance of entomology and insects.

He explains that these are characterised by a tendency for the general public to scream and/or flinch when insects enter their personal space, to kill insects when found and a failure by the majority of the population to appreciate the beauty and wonder of insects (see also Leather 2009, 2013; Leather & Quicke 2009, 2010). This is not a recent phenomenon and Simon quotes the following: "No science is so generally slighted, ignored, and misunderstood as is Entomology. Hysterical humanitarians, novelists, poets, political agitators, classical students, speak in terms of contempt or horror of the "fly-hunters"" (Anonymous 1882). Insects are to blame. They are even politically aware: in the annual conference of the CBI in November 2016, the then Prime Minister Theresa May was dive-bombed by a "small dark moth" when she was giving a speech and then she started coughing in some discomfort.[11] Someone left the lights on in the Stade de France the night before the Euro 2016 football final and swarms of the migrant Silver Y Moth flew around the stadium, most famously landing on Christiano Ronaldo's face – the headlines the following day were an "irritating bug" "a plague of moths", even "savage moth attacks", with the English referee Marc Clattenburg "under attack."

Within our possession/ownership
This is an ancient view of western civilization. "And God said, Let us make man in our image, after our likeness: and let them have dominion over the fish of the sea, and over the fowl of the air, and over the cattle, and over all the earth, and over every creeping thing that creepeth upon the earth." Genesis 1:26 (*King James Bible*). We can contrast this for example with the view of the native peoples of America, as expressed by James Fenimore Cooper in *The Last of the Mohicans* where the young American colonist Major Duncan Heyward domesticates animals in his mind and learns to achieve dominance over wild creature in a number of diverse ways – with

10. https://simonleather.wordpress.com/2015/02/18/entomyopia-and-entoalexia-two-potentially-life-threatening-conditions/
11. *Daily Telegraph* 22 November 2016; in fact the "moth" was a Small Tortoiseshell butterfly.

whips, bridles, collars, leashes and fences - whereas in contrast Chingachgook, the last pure-blooded Mohican, hides in a beaver lodge and pokes his head out as the Huron Magua passes by with his warriors. The beaver which pokes his head through the lodge is merely Chingachgook in disguise. Just moments after the passage of the enemy scouting party, Chingachgook steps confidently from the lodge and removes his "mask of fur." Fenimore Cooper writes that Chingachgook becomes a beaver by draping the skin of the beaver over his own shoulders and "by this method, human control over the wild animal moving from the realm of the conceptual into that of the physical….. Whereas a dog owner must tell his pet to come, sit, or roll over, Chingachgook acquires the power to both make commands and carry them out."

The earliest writers wanted to know what butterflies were for (Marren 2016). Thomas Moffet (1589) in his *Theatrum Insectorum* devoted a whole chapter to butterflies and suggested that the only point of their existence was "to adorn the world and delight the eyes of men: to brighten the countryside like so many golden jewels". Nowadays we are more prosaic so that, in the *State of Britain's Hedgehogs* (2018) by the British Hedgehog Preservation Society and the People's Trust for Endangered Species, the claim is made that hedgehogs are important because their presence indicates a healthy environment, not valued for themselves. As John Fowles writes, in his foreword to *Collectors Items* by Salway (1996), "We can never begin to understand nature, and certainly will never respect it until we disassociate the wild from the notion of usability."

Coe in his 2015 novel *Number 11* discusses the value of human rather than animal life: the quality of human life can be valued or priced. Nothing says Laura Harvey "is important unless you can put a price on it." Even human emotion. As Rachel Wells says: "I am starting to realise that there are people around us who look normal from the outside but ….. they're not like the rest of us … They're like androids, or zombies." If we only value human life in a monetary sense, how can we value animal and plant life in any way other than in pounds, dollars or euros?[12]

Much of the talk is about ecosystem services[13] and natural capital, i.e. "those elements of the natural environment which provide valuable goods and services to people, such as the stock of forests, water, land, minerals and oceans."[14] In the case of wildlife, for example, there are existing targets and regulations for the conservation of certain species and habitats in European Union and national level designations. A simple approach to incorporating impacts which cannot be *valued*

12. Or perhaps in kuna, as I write this in Croatia below the spectacular Biokova National Park; even here the Park is mainly valued for recreation (cycling, walking, climbing) and hunting.
13. There is an interesting paper on ecosystem services by Didham, Leather & Basset (2016) on the pitfalls of a full commodification of nature where massive individual-level trait variability and adaptive plasticity in relation to environment is ignored.
14. The Natural Capital Committee (NCC) which oversees a national 25 year Environmental Plan. In my early days, the NCC stood for the Nature Conservancy Council, when we had a simplistic view of protecting wildlife for its own sake.

robustly[15] is to ensure that proposed investments do not have effects which run counter to those existing targets and regulations, and that instead they secure them or improve their status. It is recognised that the value of changes to biodiversity is particularly difficult to assess (Maddison & Day 2014).

Craig Venter claimed in 2010 to have created artificial life, although in fact his team modified an existing life form by synthesising DNA encoding the entire genome of a bacterial pathogen known as *Mycoplasma mycoides* which causes a disease in goats. They injected their synthesised genome into a living bacterial cell and managed to persuade it to replace its original chromosome with their synthesised version (Al-Khalili & McFadden 2014). Venter is well known for attempting to patent genes, perhaps the ultimate expression of ownership; the attempt was abandoned following a major outcry. I am determined that my DNA belongs to me.

Berger (1977) asks why are animals in a zoo less than domesticated animals? We possess them physically but not mentally. Scruton (1996) suggests that there is something ignoble about "a wild creature in conditions of total safety, when the poor creature, raging against the gaping crowd of spectators, cannot punish their insolence with its teeth and claws." Leopards pace up and down their narrow cages, going mad, and in Quito Zoo[16] when I visited many years ago Red Pandas lay motionless, cold and starving on hard concrete – the soldiers who staffed the military-run zoo watched the visitors not the animals – I felt that I was the captive. In Pilanesberg National Park I got out of the hire car, which I admit was rather stupid, to see three lions hunting a warthog in a valley below the road, keeping equidistant spacing between them and moving to cut off its escape. At last, real wild action in what had seemed to me to be a big organised playground for tourists who mainly wanted to take photos of their friends in exotic places. But then I saw the large tag on the lead lion's neck, so that she could be monitored and watched and GPS tracked at all times, and the wildness had disappeared. We (Gary and I)[17] saw a large White Rhinoceros with calf and again I got out of the car and crept near to take a close-up photo. A warden saw me and immediately ordered me back into the car; I had been lulled into a state of calm by the zoo-like nature of the winding drive through the beige dried landscape, mostly deserted and apparently without animals. The stationary rhino was deceptively docile – she could have charged suddenly and without warning. The real wildness was in the male elephant standing proud in the middle of the road daring us to drive up close, and in a different way gambling in Sun City (where I lost several hundred rand).

I have never seen Snow Leopards but watching one of these beautiful lonely animals being tagged on a BBC wildlife programme my first thought was one of

15. My italics.
16. Now closed; there is a new zoo, outside Quito, named Zoológico de Quito, managed by the Zoological Foundation of Ecuador and which is, according to its website, a refuge for animals that have been victims of wildlife illegal trade or hunting attempts.
17. Gary Pilkington, manager of the brilliant Marsland nature reserve on the Cornwall/Devon border.

dismay. Two leopards were given names – Pahlawan and Khani Wakhai – and kept track of as they each travelled for over 70 miles across the mountains in the Hindu Kush. I understand that the knowledge gained may help inform conservation programmes, providing information on hunting and mating territories, but does the presence of this large collar interfere with the animal's successful predatory or camouflage behaviour, does it affect mating behaviour, does it hurt; does the knowledge gained justify the repeated capture and interference by humans? But most of all, we are claiming ownership of this proud independent animal …

A simpler possession includes twitching – ticking the birds we have seen, or the moths and butterflies, or perhaps photographing them to retain them in our memory (although it has the opposite effect as we remember the photo not the real being). The Lepidoptera community set moths, arranging them in taxonomic order in their cabinets, exhibiting them at exhibitions; in this way the collector can see what species he (and it is most often a he) still has to collect (as defined by the gaps in his collection) and can impress and inform other collectors at exhibitions. With each personally caught specimen (not those purchased or exchanged) there is a story attached, to place the specimen in context. Thus I can select a particular specimen of a Sandhill Rustic moth collected at Inch on the Dingle peninsula in Ireland and tell the story of leaving a generator running a moth lamp overnight lighting up the base of the cliffs whilst Steve Church and I ate in the beach café with sand blowing on the windows before retiring to our hotel in Dingle miles away to the west, returning after breakfast to find the generator still there, still running and the moth trap with dark Sandhill Rustic moths clinging to the egg boxes.[18]

Of course, many collectors simply buy their specimens. There are several reasons for buying specimens: in particular you might not get the chance to visit the site and the species may no longer be available; you may want to rear the species and learn about its life cycle. An old specimen may have historic value, perhaps as the first specimen ever caught, or perhaps the last specimen before the species became extinct in the UK. Robert Goodden[19] used to say that he could tell where the extinct forms of the Large Blue butterfly came from by looking at their colour; now the species has been introduced from Sweden and re-introduced (and flown on its own) from the introduction sites to a range of sites in Somerset and Gloucestershire, these old historic colour forms help reveal the history of this iconic species.[20]
The interest in buying butterflies and moths dates back over 100 years. The Netted Carpet moth, first found in 1856 in the Lake District, was considered as a commodity and there was considerable demand for specimens for completeness (Hancock 2018). H. Murray & Son of Carnforth[21] advertised themselves as

18. Almost anywhere in England the generator would have disappeared over night.
19. Robert Goodden ran the butterfly farm at Over Compton near Sherborne and took over the Lullingstone Silk Farm when it moved from Lullingstone in Kent (see Chapter 4).
20. The Large Blue is not collectable as it is legally protected by Wildlife and Countryside Act 1981 (as amended in 2007).
21. Carnforth is now known in entomological circles for the rare psychid moth Bankesia conspur-

"Naturalists and Specialists in Pictorial Taxidermy" (although their main work was saddlery) and collected Netted Carpets for sale at 14 shillings each in 1890. Murray planted a patch of the larval foodplant Touch-me-not Balsam as fresh food for his larvae. The value of each specimen was based at least partly on rarity and the difficulty of obtaining the specimens; values had to be calculated for exchanges. There were many examples of specimens sold as British which actually had a foreign provenance.

An interesting slant on collecting and exhibiting specimens was the so-called Sodium Tungstate affair. The annual exhibition of the British Entomological and Natural History Society (founded in 1872) is held in London every November, and is a place to meet fellow entomologists, exchange gossip and information on what is happening in the entomological world, what new species have been described, what is new to Britain etc. Exhibits are laid out on tables, divided into British and foreign exhibits, several tables for moths, some for beetles, bugs and flies etc., and perhaps one table for British butterflies as few people collect these nowadays. In 2015, there was an exhibit of two specimens of Silver-washed Fritillary resulting from pupae injected at a particular time with small quantities of sodium tungstate and these showed distinct aberrations[22]; the aim was to explore the effect of chemical shocks to pupae at various time intervals. Other specimens (not exhibited) had been injected at different times and these had emerged successfully and produced normal adults. The same person had exhibited similarly produced Peacock butterfly aberrations at the 2014 Exhibition. Two people objected to this experiment on the basis that such experiments cannot, in any way, claim to have any scientific value, because unlike experiments on the effect of temperature changes on pupae which could occur in the wild and so might explain certain 'varieties', no pupa would be subject to being injected with a chemical in the wild. My own initial view on this was that in a way this showed an inappropriate sense of ownership of living things and served no real scientific purpose. This matter was fully discussed at the BENHS Council which decided on 8th September 2016 that exhibits involving experimentation should be accompanied by full scientific explanations. I began to change my mind; at first I thought that the experiments were inappropriate but, on further consideration, I began to see that prevention of exhibits that we don't agree with may be seen as the "thin end of the wedge" and may lead to further attacks on the practice of exhibiting dead specimens. So, although my first view was against inappropriate actions based on a proprietorial sense of ownership, my later considered view was that it was an example of extending our own views onto animals, and in particular onto insects of limited intellectual capacity.

---

catella; the cases (and occasionally male moths) are mainly found on a whitewashed wall on the platform that carries the branch line running to Barrow in Furness and the Cumbrian coast (Steve Palmer *pers. comm.*).
22. *British Journal of Entomology Volume* **29**(1): 13.

An extension of ourselves

We appear to be losing the sense of difference between us and animals.[23] When the London housewife Barbara Carter won a "grant a wish" charity contest in 1976, she said she wanted to kiss and cuddle a lion. For her prize she was taken to the lions' compound at the Safari Park at Bewdley Worcestershire. As she bent forward to stroke the lioness, Suki, it pounced and dragged her to the ground. She was rushed to hospital in a state of shock with throat wounds. The park wardens said: "We seem to have made a bad error of judgment." Perhaps the zoo environment had lulled the wardens into viewing the lioness as a pet.[24]

Timothy Treadwell (the Grizzly Man) thought he had bridged the gap between human and bear and lived amongst a group of Grizzly Bears in Alaska. He hadn't of course – one of the bears turned on him as shown by his own video footage …

When in 2015 Cecil the Lion was shot with a bow and arrow[25] by Walter Palmer, a 55 year-old dentist from Minnesota, paying $65,000 for the privilege, there was huge worldwide condemnation with over four million tweets in a matter of days. Cecil was 13 years old and had become a major tourist attraction in Matabeleland, Zimbabwe. Cecil's six-year-old male offspring – named Xanda – was also killed in its prime by a big game trophy hunter in Zimbabwe. By giving these animals names we are attributing a sense of individuality, uniqueness and value to them. Xanda was wearing an electronic tag and was being monitored; both animals were objective parts of long-term university research programmes. We might think that the uproar over these killings was a sign of a worldwide interest in nature conservation – but the more realistic interpretation is that it is a worldwide expression of anthropomorphism.

Are we in danger of losing contact with reality? When a poisonous non-native Black Widow Spider was found in Portlethen, Aberdeen, in a crate imported from America, the Scottish Society for the Prevention of Cruelty to Animals were called out. Many people might have simply crushed the spider under foot, being non-native and poisonous, but SPCA are reported as saying[26] "Sadly the spider had to be put to sleep."[27] It was not the same in former times. Richard Harris as the rugby star Frank Machin in the 1963 film *This Sporting Life* watches as his landlady and lover played by Rachel Roberts dies of a brain haemorrhage; seeing a black spider

---

23. And perhaps even between us and plants – Prince Charles is well known for his habitat of talking to plants.
24. Is there a particular English sentimentality about animals? Sansom in his (2006) book *Winter in Madrid* writes that Barbara couldn't stomach the bullfights, "the big strong animal tormented and killed, horses gored and dying, kicking in the sand" to which her English husband laughs saying his Spanish friends "would think her the worst sort of English sentimentalist." I took my family to see a bullfight in Cazorla in Spain many years ago, and they all left, leaving me to watch the second half on my own.
25. Cecil was actually killed the following morning, as Palmer's arrow only wounded him.
26. *Daily Telegraph* 25 August 2018.
27. Joan Dunayer (quoted in Herzog 2011) – says "am I saying that a spider has as much right to life as an egret or a human? Yes. I see no logically consistent reason to say otherwise."

on the wall he crushes it with his fist, the ooze and legs visible under his knuckles. I cannot remember any complaints at the time about cruelty to animals.

A hermit crab called Hector has become the first hermit crab in Europe to have a bespoke 3D printed shell made from transparent acrylic for it at Blackpool's Sea Life Centre[28]; I wonder what it thinks of it – if anything at all?

Even the *New Scientist* appears to have joined the "let's call animals an extension of ourselves" club. In an article entitled *Elephants under fire*[29], explaining that across Africa an elephant is killed every 15 minutes, this slaughter is defined as genocide on the basis that elephants, which are capable of rationality and self-awareness, are not only worthy of protection as individuals but as a "people". Surviving elephants from culls show symptoms of post-traumatic distress and they have elaborate societies and relationships. The Worldwide Fund for Nature host a television advert which asks for funding to help save elephants "as one of our oldest friends."

PETA (People for the Ethical Treatment of Animals) took the photographer David Slater to court in the USA in 2018 because in 2011 he went to Sulawesi to take photos of macaques and whilst there a monkey named Naruto took a photo of itself grinning at the camera. This has become a world-famous photo. PETA claimed that Slater had infringed the monkey's copyright by releasing *Wildlife Personalities*, a self-published book of photography that included the famous monkey selfie. Wikipedia refused to take down the photo because they said the monkey owned the copyright. However, the Ninth Circuit Court of Appeals in America concluded that animals do not have legal standing under the Copyright Act and it probably only applies to humans. Interestingly, the Court went on to say that PETA seemed to employ Naruto as an unwitting pawn in its ideological goals.[30] A 2020 BBC One television programme called *Primates* – shown at peak time and narrated by Chris Packham – was presented with anthropocentric emotional overtones and called one female monkey a "single mother"– even though the females usually go off alone with their offspring and are not anything like human single mothers living on benefits in city suburbs. Then, having spent the entire programme treating monkeys as cute delightful friendly animals, at the end of the programme there was a short section on rescued gibbons in Malaysia and how important it is not to keep them as pets.

28. *The Sunday Post* 16 April 2017.
29. *New Scientist* 30 April 2016, No. 3071.
30. https://www.theverge.com/2018/4/24/17271410/monkey-selfie-naruto-slater-copyright-peta ac-cessed 1 June 2018. Case thrown out in April 2018 on the basis that PETA lack "next friend" status to bring the lawsuit on behalf of the monkey, animals in general don't have standing to sue under the Copyright Act. The Ninth Circuit concluded that the Copyright Act does not clearly state that animals can sue. The court stated: Puzzlingly, while representing to the world that "animals are not ours to eat, wear, experiment on, use for entertainment, or abuse in any other way," PETA seems to employ Naru-to as an unwitting pawn in its ideological goals. PETA's real motivation in this case was to advance its own interests, not Naruto's," and that the organisation used Naruto as a 'pawn to be manipulated on a chessboard larger than his own case.'

The Nonhuman Rights Project[31] claims to be the only civil rights organisation in the United States working to achieve actual legal rights for members of species other than humans. Their mission is to change the legal status of appropriate nonhuman animals from mere "things," which lack the capacity to possess any legal right, to "persons," (*their words*) who possess such fundamental rights as bodily integrity and bodily liberty. Their first cases were filed in 2013 on behalf of captive chimpanzees and they plan to continue to file as many lawsuits as they have funds available. They claim the recognition of the legal personhood and fundamental right to bodily liberty of individual great apes, elephants, dolphins, and whales held in captivity across the US.[32] They filed a claim under habeas corpus on behalf of the chimpanzees Hercules and Leo which were former research subjects at Stony Brook University's Department of Anatomical Sciences and the first nonhuman animals to have a habeas corpus hearing. In a complicated and protracted lawsuit, at one time (20th April 2015) it was claimed that a judge issued a writ of habeas corpus and ordered the university to defend their right to detain the chimpanzees before amending this order the following day thus removing the habeas corpus writ.

There is a long way to go in this process and a lot of legal issues, not least the following:

- What is the standing of conservation or legal organisations acting for animals with which they cannot intelligently communicate and which therefore cannot agree to being legally represented? If animals have rights, we would require their consent in taking them into captivity, training them, domesticating them, acting on their behalf (Scruton 1996).

- If animals have rights, should they have duties? Surely if the fox has rights, it would be duty bound to respect the rights of other animals – the right to life of a chicken for example. Foxes – and a lot of other predators – would be condemned as criminal (Scruton 1996). Or should mankind be seen as benevolent masters, making decisions on behalf of wildlife – we certainly have a duty of care for animals which we make dependent on us for their survival and well-being.

- Which animals should be included? It should be noted that invertebrate orders thought to suffer or feel significant pain are the Decapoda (crabs, lobsters, crayfish, prawns and shrimps) and Cephalopoda (squid, octopus, nautilus) and Crustacean Compassion[33] believe that decapods should

---

31. http://www.nonhumanrightsproject.org/
32. It is interesting that several great apes at San Diego Zoo were given experimental covid-19 vaccines, including an orangutan named Karen (which had been the first great ape to have had open-heart surgery in 1994) and a 49-year old silverback gorilla called Winston which had started coughing. Eight gorillas had tested positive for covid. None were asked if they wanted to be vaccinated. *Daily Telegraph* 5 March 2021.
33. https://www.crustaceancompassion.org.uk/

be treated more humanely and receive full protection under UK animal welfare law, as they are in some other countries such as Norway and Switzerland. The Animals (Scientific Procedures) Act 1986 already provides in the UK welfare protection for the Common Octopus in the course of experimental work. In an interesting paper by Fischer & Larson (2019) it is suggested that even insects are conscious and the authors encourage entomologists to revisit their ethical collection codes, especially in the use of malaise traps (which indiscriminately collect and kill flying insects).

- Should intelligence be the key factor in recognising legal rights for animals, or should it be beauty, cuddliness, majesty? Insects do not learn from experience. The moth flies to the moth trap regardless of the consequences, as this is what happens when it perceives ultra-violet light (Spalding 2019); it learns nothing from the experience and the next evening will return. "Moths end life as they began it, in a state of cognitive innocence from which no experience can tempt them" (Scruton 1996). On the other hand, there are many examples of intelligence in animals, but usually under laboratory conditions. In an interesting experiment, outlined by Troscianko & Rutz (2015), New Caledonian crows were recorded by bird-borne video cameras and shown to manufacture and use hooked stick tools (e.g. from live branches of Paperbark *Melaleuca* species) for foraging for food on the forest floor. Perhaps these birds should be legally represented to see if they agree to being studied in this way?

There is a real difference in perception of the rights of animals compared with those of plants. I organised and took part with Graham Collins in a year-long study of the invertebrates of an extensive sand dune system on the north coast of the UK. As part of this study, and in addition to using sweep nets, butterfly nets, light traps, suction traps and general searching (e.g. under stones), we erected three malaise traps at different heights along a profile across the dunes, from sea to inland edge. The malaise traps are interception traps (unlike light traps for example, which distort invertebrate behaviour and attract flying insects) and these three occupied an immeasurably tiny fraction of the dune system. They work by directing invertebrates caught in the trap upwards towards a killing bottle, so all captured specimens are killed. The lowest malaise trap, which was in a private part of the dunes, collected large numbers of Dune Chafer beetle and Silver-studded Blues, as both were abundant in this area. The Silver-studded Blue is an especially lovely butterfly. On the third collection visit, we found that the malaise trap had been dismantled, effectively ruining part of our experiment where we were comparing catches at different seasons and at different heights. It is almost certain that the trap was dismantled by a bryologist who had complained at a previous meeting about killing butterflies, even though as a bryologist she always carried a sharp knife so that she could cut off sample sections from mosses and liverworts to take them back home to identify under the microscope.[34] But then mosses and liverworts are certainly less intelligent than butterflies.

A different take on nature as an extension of ourselves is by the charity People Need Nature, set up to promote nature as a source of inspiration, for the emotional and spiritual benefits nature provides us, and the value of nature on public land. Their strapline[35] is *Nature doesn't need human beings – it will survive without us*. This is true of course (see Chapter 6), and this is partly what this book is about – although "Nature" may well survive in a completely different way without man's interference. However, they go on to say that *We need nature to thrive and survive.* So they see Nature as separate from Mankind but essential to our survival. However, they do not see Nature in an immaculate alien way, but rather as something we can use and gain from. In this way, if mankind uses nature as they seem to suggest, nature may be harmed.

Representing aspects of our psyche and civilization
Many books and articles have been written about how animals and to a lesser extent plants are taken to represent aspects of the spiritual world and more recently our increasing alienation from the real world outside our houses, villages and cities. The present book aims mainly to avoid these themes but a few are listed here for completeness:

- Butterflies may reflect the presence of God. For butterflies "to gaze enquiringly at such elegance……. is to acknowledge and adore the imprint of the art of God" (Ray, 1710).
- Butterflies may represent the spirits of the dead, as in the tale of Liang Shan-po and Zhu Ying-tai, where their spirits were seen flying out of their tomb "gracefully dancing against the rainbow" (Rothschild 1991).
- Butterflies out of place as contrasts with human misery, as in the two white butterflies flying far above the prisoners in the prison yard in Van Gogh's 1890 painting *The Prison Courtyard*.
- Moths may represent the soul of the departed, as in the Superstitious Man's Story by Thomas Hardy (1894) where death is confirmed when a large white moth flies out of a man's mouth, as the soul escaping the body.[36]
- Red poppies are in the UK a sign of respect for the dead of the First World War as celebrated in Remembrance Sunday but David Cameron found in China in 2010 that they symbolised the opium trade and the two wars that

---

34. Why is it worse to kill a butterfly than a beetle or fly, and why is it better to dig up a moss for scientific examination than use malaise traps for finding new species on nature reserves? Our year-long study produced records for over 1000 invertebrate species for this site. However, there is a move to reduce the use of malaise traps in entomological surveys to reduce the moral risk associated with collection, particularly since it is difficult to know with certainty the effect on insect populations (Fischer & Larson 2019).
35. www.peopleneednature.org.uk
36. See also the anonymous poem entitled *The Soul*: "breathe his last, a trembling moth …. would glide from out his mouth and float …" (quoted from Rothschild 1991).

Britain fought to keep that trade open.[37]

- Turtles may be a sign of great historic moments or alarming omens, such as the death in Vietnam of Cu Rua, a freshwater turtle said to be 120 years old.[38]

At the same time, artists may use wild things from nature as a commentary on our civilization. These are more successful on some occasions than on others. The Chinese artist Ai Weiwei installed his sculpture *Tree* in the courtyard of the Royal Academy in 2015. In what seems to me a rather pointless exercise the "tree" was made from dead wood brought down from the mountains of southern China and sold in the markets of Jingdezhen. In the rather fanciful language of those who see the words associated with an artwork as more important than the art itself,[39] *Tree* celebrates indigenous Chinese customs, evokes traditional Chinese Zen gardens and can be read as a reference to the Taoist ideal of harmony – unifying the work of man with nature as well as linking the earth and the sky. It draws attention to the conceptual relationship between material and form in sculpture and the country's rapid urbanisation and economic growth, which have resulted in damage to the natural environment and the suppression of traditional culture. In addition, the act of bringing together numerous individual branches to create a whole can be read as symbolic of the relationship between the individual and society, a broader issue but one which has particular resonance in a Chinese context. (I am pleased to report that "The viewer is not led to believe this is a natural living tree.") There are more than one *Tree*. The *Tree* in the Royal Academy in 2015 was inspected by the Government's chief plant health officer who noticed beetle exit holes in the wooden structure; unfortunately the sculpture had been made from wood where the Asian Longhorn beetle, which is major pest of wood, is rife.[40] The Royal Academy was forced to close and fumigate the artwork – and thus did real wildlife triumph over art. (The Forestry Commission inspected the work and found no signs of active infestation).

More outlandish than Ai Weiwei was the German Conceptual Artist Joseph Beuys who flew especially to New York in 1974 for a meeting with a live coyote in a performance work *I Like America and America Likes Me*.[41] For three days he spent eight hours living and communing with the coyote, which for him was a potent symbol of America's past as sacred to native Americans. Beuys saw the coyote as representing America's spirit animal as well as being the archetypal trickster.[42] In contrast, the *Wall Street Journal* represented contemporary America and Beuys made two piles of these every day to be torn by or urinated on by the coyote as a statement on contemporary America. Beuys attempted to make eye contact

37. The prime minister was asked to remove his poppy before meeting the Chinese president. He refused. Cameron, D. 2019. *For the Record*. William Collins. London.
38. *Daily Telegraph* 21 January 2016.
39. Taken from the Tate Gallery https://www.tate.org.uk/art/artworks/ai-tree-t14630
40. *Daily Telegraph* 10 November 2018.
41. https://www.tate.org.uk/art/artworks/beuys-coyote-ar00733
42. The coyote was considered by some native Americans to be the chief animal of the age before humans, and viewed as a creator, lover, magician, glutton and trickster https://www.britannica.com/topic/Coyote-mythology

with the coyote whilst gesticulating wildly at it with hands and stick (perhaps for self defence). What the coyote thought of it all is not known, but apparently its behaviour alternated between hostility and docility. The art work can be read as a plea for creating a dialogue between the present and the past. Joseph Beuys died in 1986. I'm not sure when the caged coyote died but the coyote breed lives on, despite thousands being killed each year, perhaps a symbol of its resilience and adaptation to modern America.

In this book I attempt to expand on our view of species and consider the integrity of their existence. The integrity of wildlife (plants and animals) is based on many things: their historical context, their nativeness, the pace of their evolution (past and future), their adaptation to man's environment and their ability for self-propelled movement. Our view of these species is based on our different perceptions and our upbringing. Species are also individuals acting independently rather than fitting into their definitions prepared by Man and as independent beings may surprise us by their development (in plants) or by their actions (in animals). These perceptions have critical effect on our attempts at successful nature conservation and justification of effort based on wildlife for people.[43] We may consider this as an existentialist view of wildlife – and I did consider entitling this book *The Existentialist Species* – but it seems to me that no-one really knows what existentialism is; based as it is on freedom of movement, thought and personality it can mean many different things to many different persons. Jean Paul Sartre in a 1945 lecture said "I am my own freedom". More realistically, we are "only free within situations, which can include factors within my own biology and psychology as well as physical, historical and social variables of the world into which I have been thrown" (Bakewell 2016). It is partly a question of authenticity based on understanding, which can "awaken us to ways of living more authentic lives" (Bakewell 2016). So in this book I am attempting to investigate the authenticity of species without the weighty mantle of human interpretation upon them. I do not attempt to discuss freedom of action, how much freedom a chimpanzee has compared to a beetle. I instead look at species within their authentic habitats.

---

43. For a scientific review of these ideas see for example *Circle the bandwagons – challenges mount against the theoretical foundations of applied functional trait and ecosystem service research* by Didham, Leather & Basset (2016) who point to the overwhelming evidence for massive individu-al–level trait variability and what they call "the stuff of natural selection" – selective pressures acting on the performance and fitness of individuals with different suites of traits responding to varying environments and biotic interactions. They point to three societal dilemmas: (i) the public dilemma (invertebrates and their ecological services are mostly unknown to the general public); (ii) the politi-cal dilemma (policymakers are mostly unaware of invertebrate conservation problems) and (iii) the scientific dilemma (basic science on invertebrates is limited) and to four contributing scientific short-falls: (iv) the Linnean shortfall (most species are undescribed), (v) the Wallacean shortfall (species' geographic distributions are poorly known), (vi) the Prestonian shortfall (spatio-temporal variation in population abundances are poorly known), and (vii) the Hutchinsonian shortfall (species life histories and sensitivities to habitat change are largely unknown).

CHAPTER 2. SPECIES IN HISTORICAL CONTINUUM

In the 1962 film *Lonely are the Brave* the central character[44] is a ranch hand in New Mexico who finds it difficult to come to terms with modern life; he rides his horse Whiskey across the wild landscape, works and sleeps where he can. Pursued by the police and attempting to reach Mexico where he will be safe, he crosses Highway 66 at night but is blinded by the lights of a lorry and knocked down. The Sheriff refuses to identify him as the pursued criminal – he sympathises with him as a man out of place and of time. We live in the context of our time, some people more than others – and many people as they get older feel more out of touch with modern society and lose their historical connection with the land.

Wild things, animals and even plants, exist within the historical context of their presence. We know that Small Tortoiseshell butterflies were flying in the 16th century from a single dry, unpinned specimen found loose inside a manuscript (Thomas Moffet's *Theatrum Insectorum* dating from about 1590), with no head and no abdomen, but with undamaged wings with faded colours (the brown colours can be seen as can the venation) and almost translucent (Marren & Warren 2017). The oldest pinned butterfly is probably the Bath White collected by William Vernon in 1702 and preserved in the Hope Entomological Collections at Oxford. Species exist in a population continuum over time – unless like the Dodo in 1681 they became extinct (also in the Hope Museum).[45] As long ago as 1869, Alfred Russell Wallace recognised that the wildlife of an area depends as much or even more on the history of the country as on its main physical and climatological features (Wallace 1869). Species are historical entities (Dennis & Schmitt 2009) on the evolutionary scale but also on the geographical scale. To understand a species we need to know why it is where it is and where it will be in years to come; species exist in a population continuum over time.[46] How did it get there, where was it before, what does its history tell us about its chances of survival? This is true of man of course[47] and of butterflies and all wildlife (Dennis & Schmitt 2009). Their presence tells us about the history of their habitat and the wider landscape. Nabokov said in a *Playboy* interview in 1964[48]:

---

44. Played by Kirk Douglas.
45. As bones and soft tissue; Darren Mann let me hold the bone, so light you could hardly feel it was there.
46. Including of course, deep geological time, as shown by the palaeogeographical history of their ancestors from evidence in the fossil record. For invertebrates, such as spiders and insects, this is most notable in fossils preserved in amber tens of millions of years old. Many of the extinct species are barely distinguishable from their modern counterparts (e.g. Penney 2016).
47. "To be ignorant of what occurred before you were born is to remain always a child. For what is the worth of human life, unless it is woven into the life of our ancestors by the records of history." Cicero (46BC).
48. Toffler, Alvin: "Playboy Interview: Vladimir Nabokov". *Playboy* (Chicago, IL), 11 (1), Jan 1964, pp. 35–41, 44–45.

"butterfly …. that you now see on the wing, in their natural surroundings, among plants and minerals that acquire a mysterious magic through the intimate association with the rarities they produce and support, so that a given landscape lies twice: as a delightful wilderness in its own right and as the haunt of a certain butterfly or moth."

There is a kind of naturalist who can go onto a site and predict what species will be present. Perhaps he or she will look at the plants and say that because European Gorse is present Green Hairstreaks will be abundant at suitable times of year. Quite often he will be correct – but perhaps less in modern times in an increasingly fragmented landscape where isolated populations may die out with little chance of recolonisation of the habitat. But this naturalist ignores two things: he ignores the particular specialisations of the species concerned and he ignores the historical factors that have led to its presence – or absence.

Thus the larvae of the Scarce Blackneck moth feed on Wood Vetch,[49] which is a scrambling or climbing perennial growing to about two metres high. The plant occurs locally throughout much of Britain chiefly in open woods and on woodland edges (Preston *et al.* 2002), but also on rough ungrazed grassland on cliffs, wooded gorges, shingle, screes and railway banks. However, in the UK the moth is confined to the northern coasts of Cornwall, Devon and Somerset[50] although it is widespread on sparsely vegetated slopes on continental Europe from Scandinavia southwards to Crete. We are not sure of the causes of this restricted distribution but it could be due to a combination of factors including:

- Historical factors – The Scarce Blackneck was part of a wave of wildlife re-colonisation events into Britain over hundreds of years after the last ice age when during the last glacial maximum much of Britain would have been covered by ice sheet, with permafrost to the south.

- Geographical factors – High spring and summer temperatures may be necessary for the larvae to eat and for the adult moths to mate and lay eggs. Temperature readings taken by me at a coastal Scarce Blackneck site in Cornwall between 1st April and 31st August 2001 showed a maximum reading of 35.7°C and a minimum of 3.4°C. The average temperature during the flight period (roughly 20th July to 31st August) was 18°C; maximum daytime temperatures during this period ranged from 16–34°C against minimum night time temperatures of 10–19°C. By comparison, readings taken at a site about 0.3km inland were much cooler (maximum 20.5°C and minimum 3.9°C). The daily range of temperatures was greater at the coastal sites, cooling down more at night but with higher temperatures on exposed sites with sparse vegetation during the day (Spalding 2003).

49. It has also been found on Tufted Vetch (Henwood, Spalding & McCormick 2004).
50. Spalding (2003).

There are many species which have a distribution that is hard for us to understand. Here are a few examples – the reasons are often due to historical factors:

- The presence of a colony of Marsh Fritillary in the Midlands which was dissimilar genetically to adjacent populations. This was discovered when sampling Marsh Fritillaries in the UK (Joyce & Pullin 2001). In fact, it turned out that this colony was the result of a deliberate introduction of Marsh Fritillaries from France.[51] [52]

- The Thyme Lace Bug, found on cliffs where Wild Thyme occurs and only found in Britain on the coast of west Cornwall; the Cornish population is flightless and so a poor coloniser, and assumed to be relics from an interglacial period (Alexander 2008) although its flightless state might be a more recent adaptation to its confined coastal existence.

- The Lesser White-toothed Shrew, also known as the Scilly Shrew, has a very wide distribution, ranging from southern Europe into Asia and the northern parts of Africa but in the British Isles is only found on the Isles of Scilly and two of the Channel Islands, Jersey and Sark (Harris & Yalden 2008). They are believed to have been present on Scilly since at least the Bronze Age, possible having been introduced by early traders. They are the only species of shrew which occurs on the Isles of Scilly and have recently seen a large population increase on the islands of St Ages and Gugh as a result of the removal of rats as part of a Seabird Recovery Project (see also Chapter 4).

- Black Hairstreak butterflies are limited to heavy clays between Oxfordshire and Peterborough even though their foodplant Blackthorn is widespread and common throughout Britain; one theory explaining its restricted distribution is that it occurs in areas where the historic management of the Royal game forests was carried out on a long coppice rotation of 20–40 years which provided continuous areas of large mature Blackthorn which the butterfly prefers. Very similar to the White-letter Hairstreak, and very elusive as it skulks around Blackthorn bushes rarely flying, its presence in Britain was only discovered in 1828 (and initially thought to be White-letter Hairstreak). This butterfly is not a great wanderer and an entire colony will often confine itself to a single area within a wood, despite there being suitable habitat nearby. The inability to colonise new areas at a

51. I met the lead author Domino Joyce at a Butterfly Conservation Symposium many years ago and in the pub afterwards she told me all about horizontal starch gel electrophoresis – now an out-of-date process but very valuable for me then in my studies on Sandhill Rustic moths.
52. Genetic analysis can show the recent history of introductions; for example, Dormice were re-introduced in 2001 into Wych in Cheshire from the Isle of Wight over 130km away, and this still shows in the genetic similarity of the two populations (Combe *et al.* 2016).

pace in balance with habitat loss may partially explain the scarcity of this species.[53]

- The Brown Diving Beetle. This is a small water beetle about 9mm in length and difficult to identify by the non-expert. It is found in gravel beds at the edges of streams, often deep within the gravel, feeding on small invertebrates. It is unable to fly and therefore colonisation of new habitats is difficult. It is not cold hardy, and is on the edge of its global range in Britain (Calosi *et al.* 2008). Nationally it is very rare, being restricted to southern Britain and having since 1970 been recorded from west Cornwall, the New Forest and the River Frome in Dorset. In Cornwall, there are old records from the Lizard, Gwithian, Porthtowan and in the Carnon Valley but it is currently known in Cornwall only from the Portreath Stream. It is interesting to note that Portreath Stream is devoid of fish, possibly due to high levels of metal contamination, which might aid the survival of this beetle here due to lack of predators.

- The distribution of burnet moths in Britain. There are more burnet moth species in Scotland than in the rest of Britain, but only one of these (Scotch Burnet) is associated with the high mountains. It is possible that these species colonised Britain after the last ice age, spreading into Scotland during a warm period 6–7000 years ago and then, as the climate cooled again, becoming isolated in warm refugia on basalt soils on the west Highland coasts often sheltered by coastal cliffs (Ravenscroft & Young 1996).

- The Irish China-Mark. This small moth was found 2017 in County Kildare in a calcareous marsh associated with a thermal mineral spring, the first record for Ireland and Britain. It is found on continental Europe from Germany to Greece occupying wetlands and small streams. Strickland (2019) suggests that it is possibly native, perhaps surviving here due to the micro-climate of the site. This species joins a list of other moths found in Ireland but unknown in mainland Britain: Burren Green, Irish Annulet and White Prominent.

The absence of species from potentially suitable sites may be harder to understand. In some cases, a habitat looks perfect for a species but it is absent from the site. Often this will be because the habitat was destroyed at some time and, although now recovered in some ways, some of the key species have never recolonised. Here are a few possible examples:

- Wistman's Wood on Dartmoor. This wood is a remnant of a once extensive dwarf oak woodland that covered large parts of Dartmoor. Although now fenced off, the wood had previously been open to sheep grazing; as a result

---

53. https://www.ukbutterflies.co.uk/species.php?species=pruni

my moth list when light trapping was poorer than expected although we did find the uncommon moth *Elegia simillela*.[54]

- Curnach Hazel Wood at Applecross. I ran a small actinic light moth trap here but found only common moths such as Nut Tree Tussock and Scalloped Hazel; these results may indicate that at some point the habitat was largely destroyed.

- Suscinio dunes, Brittany. There is an old 1924 record of the Sandhill Rustic moth from these dunes (Lhomme 1925, 1926) and when I visited the site with my friend Eric Drouet in September 2006 the dunes looked perfectly suitable for the moth, with extensive foredune facing west with abundant vigorous Sand Couch Grass (the larval foodplant) over quartz sand. However, on close inspection the dune system appeared to be an artificial bank built as a defence against the sea, with a simple shape, showing no dynamic structure and with little bare ground; a dune conservation management scheme was in place, with a paling fence on the seaward side erected to prevent access and probably to catch the sand. Eric told me that the dune habitat had probably been previously almost destroyed by people and the moth would have disappeared during this period, with little chance of recolonisation since the nearest known colonies are over 300km away.[55]

Some species may be considered as historical indicator species.[56] These are species the presence of which indicates that a habitat has been unaltered for many years or was once more extensive, and the species has been present for a long time. They may be less mobile species, such as flightless insects, they may be specialist species with a close link to particular ancient habitats, they may be relict species, i.e. species which were more widespread in the past and which now occur in a fraction of their former range. These are species which may not be able to adapt to changing conditions and which need to move to new areas in order to survive. The Mottled Grasshopper is a good example. It flies up when disturbed and then round in a semi-circle to the same spot. It is associated with hot open ground and its presence indicates habitat continuity (Spalding & Haes 1995).

---

54. I ran light trap here on several occasions with permission from the relevant authorities. It was a huge task to take the trap and a heavy generator across the moor as it was impossible to drive to the wood. One night we were there coincided with a break-out from Dartmoor Prison and we wondered whether we would see an escaped prisoner creeping past – unlikely as our mercury vapour lights were bright enough to scare anyone away. Another night coincided with the Perseid meteor shower and in the remote darkness we watched the comets cross the sky. There is an interesting optical illusion across the valley where the water in the mining leat appears to flow uphill.

55. The nearest known colonies are Loe Bar, Cornwall c300km; La Teste, Gironde 345km; Saclas, Ile-de-France 370km.

56. As well as geographical indicators: a video showing left wing guerrillas in Colombia endorsing a candidate in Ecuador's presidential election was shown to be false by a bird expert who heard the song of the Pale-browed Tinamou which only occurs in Ecuador and Peru, not Colombia, a ground-dwelling bird more often heard than seen. *Daily Telegraph* 10 February 2021.

In some cases we can see from the fossil record that species have disappeared, perhaps due to climate changes or the actions of Man. Cave Bears, Cave Lion, Scimitar-toothed Cat, Woolly Mammoth, Woolly Rhino and Hyena, all once occupied Kents Cavern in Torquay but have now long since gone.[57] Even small insects can provide clues as to past species distributions, especially beetles which have hard elytra and which form abundant fossils in Quaternary deposits laid down under freshwater or terrestrial conditions. Cope (1997) found that beetles display a remarkable degree of evolutionary stability so that the species composition of fossil assemblages resembles that of modern beetle communities. As a consequence, he could use the changing geographical distribution of beetles to provide clues as to changes in climate during the last glacial stage (from around 70,000 to about 10,000 years ago); at times Asiatic beetles were present in the UK indicating that the climate was continental. At other times, the Loch Lomond Stadial between 11,000 and 10,000 years ago saw the return of arctic faunas to the British Isles even as far south as Cornwall. Good examples of beetles found in Britain as fossil remains are the dung beetle *Aphodius holdereri*, formerly found in the UK from between 25,000 and 40,000 years ago but now found only between 3000 and 5000 metres up on the high Tibetan Plateau (where it can survive without competition from other dung beetles) and the rove beetle *Tachinus caelatus* which was common in England in the glacial period but which today lives in the mountains west of Ulan Bator in Mongolia (Kolbert 2014).

Where we have both genetic data and fossil record[58] it can be easier to determine past and present distributions. In the past (between 60,000 and 25,000 years ago), as shown by the fossil record, Red Deer occurred in southern England until the onset of ice caused them to retreat to southern Europe (Sommer & Zachos 2009). Between 14,700 and 12,650 years ago, this situation completely changed with a sudden range expansion into the northern regions including Britain and Ireland. During colder periods Red Deer would have retreated before establishing themselves where they are today. There is no fossil record of Roe Deer being present between 60,000 and 9000 years ago and they came into Britain later than Red Deer, arriving between 11,600–9000 years ago. Roe Deer are still absent from Ireland[59] (Harris & Yalden 2008). They now occur throughout most of the UK after nearly becoming extinct, but with a gap in the midlands; in southern England they are considered to be derived from introductions. Fallow Deer were present in Britain 250,000 years ago but became extinct during the last glaciation. They were re-introduced by the Normans in the 11th century and all free-living Fallow Deer

57. https://www.kents-cavern.co.uk/
58. Fossil Lepidoptera are extremely rare. Kristensen & Skalski (1998) estimate the total number known at some 600–700 specimens, covering about 200 million years (the oldest known fossil is *Archaeolepis mane*, described by Whalley (1985) from the Lower Lias of Dorset, England, based on a wing fragment with scales which show a similarity to the scales of the most primitive extant Lepidoptera, the Micropterigidae). Sohn *et al.* (2012) attempt to assemble all fossil records of Lepidoptera described formally or informally in the world literature; a total of 667 records dealing with at least 4568 specimens have been compiled.
59. Although it was introduced there in the 1860s and 1870s, it was "shot out" in the 1st half of the 20th century (Harris & Yalden 2008).

descend from these medieval introductions and escapes from deer parks (Harris & Yalden 2008).

In other cases, we can see that animals were present in an area – even though they have never been seen in the archaeological record – by looking at early rock art. Rock engravings in north-west Saudi Arabia suggest from more than 1400 rock engraving panels at Jubbah and Shuwaymis UNESCO world heritage rock art sites in Ha'il province, with 6618 individual depictions of wildlife, that some animals were present which have never been reported in the archaeological record, suggesting that the region has experienced many wetter periods in the past (Guagnin et al. 2018). The rock art dataset provides evidence that the distribution of Lesser Kudu, Wild Camel and African Wild Ass extended into north-west Arabia and that the engravers may have seen herds of Aurochs in the region. The presence of previously undocumented mammal species in Arabia provides new information regarding their distribution, as well as the types of habitat and vegetation that were available in prehistoric landscapes. Moreover, the presence of Kudu on the Arabian Peninsula indicates that the identification of palaeo-distributions based exclusively on faunal remains may miss key species in the Afro-Eurasian faunal exchange.

The species present in Britain have not been here all the time. There is no golden age of nature stasis when species settled down to a long-term period of stability – even before Man came and changed everything. The wildlife of Britain has developed since the last Ice Age.[60] At the height of last glacial phase 18,000 years ago[61] there was little if any wildlife present as what is now Britain was too cold; Britain was connected to the Continent until the landbridge in what is now called Doggerland (Sturt, Garrow & Bradley 2013) in the North Sea was flooded 8500 to 8200 years ago[62]. The present day distribution of moth species for example in Britain is the result of four factors (adapted from Majerus 2002[63]):

- The distribution of species in Europe, eastern Asian and North Africa about 10,000 years ago.
- Climatic changes since the last glaciation.
- The dispersal abilities of species.
- The activities of humans – changing habitats, introducing species, eliminating species, fragmenting the landscape.

During the last glacial maximum, much of Britain would have been covered by ice sheet; south of this would have been permafrost.[64] It is generally considered that

60. Man started to re-settle the British Isles about 12,000 years ago after the last ice age, having deserted what is now Britain during the last glaciation.
61. The Last Glacial Maximum refers to the period 18,000–25,000 years ago, generally the coldest period of the glacial stage in Europe.
62. There is speculation that Doggerland was finally flooded as a consequence of the Storegga slide tsunami circa 8100 years ago in a catastrophic finale to an otherwise slow process (Weninger et al. 2008).
63. Majerus considers these factors for moths, but they apply generally across many species.
64. The following account is largely taken from my book Loe Bar and the Sandhill Rustic Moth.

no wildlife species would have survived in northern Europe during that time and that species (re)colonised Britain from the southern European peninsulas which acted as full-glacial refugia[65] for many species (Hewitt 1999).[66] As the ice retreated, recolonisation of Britain by many species[67] would have been overland from mainland Europe across a land link before it was lost due to rising sea levels at some point over 8000 years ago (Sturt, Garrow & Bradley 2013). It is believed that species moved northwards as the climate warmed, reaching Britain after 14,000 years ago (Table 2.1), tracking the climate, maintaining environmental constancy not geographic constancy (Majerus 2002). The climate in Britain 13,000 years ago may well have been warmer than now (Atkinson, Briffa & Coope 1987).

Colonisation by mobile species would have been in waves, with species advancing as the ice retreated, then disappearing from Britain as the ice returned 11,000 years ago in the Younger Dryas period (e.g. Atkinson, Briffa & Coope 1987). After 1000 years, this cold spell came to an end and the polar front shifted north again, the climate warmed and vegetation advanced rapidly over Europe. By 6000 years ago, the vegetation pattern broadly resembled that of today (Hewitt 1999). Long distance dispersants would have set up colonies far ahead of the main populations, which were eliminated when the climate cooled. Then re-population followed from different refugia which may be revealed in the complex genetic make-up of present populations (e.g. Tison *et al.* 2014). Most recolonisation attempts would have been limited by climate but some by the absence of suitable foodplants or habitat suitability; species would have re-colonised in sequence e.g. for butterflies Mountain Ringlet would have re-colonised first (15 ka BP) with Green-veined White, Small Pearl-bordered Fritillary, Small Copper and Common Blue following, and the most recent being Black-veined White, Brown Hairstreak and Black Hairstreak (Dennis 1993). The last butterfly to arrive would have been the most warmth demanding species such as Lulworth Skipper and Glanville Fritillary (Dennis 1992). In contrast, Dormouse would have arrived in the UK in a single post-glacial colonisation event, about 11,000–8000 years ago, during a period of climatic stability and when woodland habitat was prevalent (e.g. in Doggerland,

65. In cold periods, the term refugia describes small pockets of micro-environmentally favourable conditions (e.g. south-facing slopes, sheltered valleys, moist river areas) where temperate species survived (Birks & Willis 2008).

66. Recent theories suggest that the situation in the last glacial maximum was complex, and that some species (woody plants and vertebrates) would have survived much further north, depending on their biogeographical traits, and that these northerly refugia extended for some species even to southern England and south-west Ireland (Bhagwat & Willis 2008). It is unlikely that thermophilic invertebrates would have survived in these refugia, although the butterfly Woodland Ringlet may have done so (Schmitt & Seitz 2001).

67. Note that for butterflies much of the dispersal would have been overseas, so that for example recolonisation of the Isle of Man would have been after it became isolated from Ireland and northern England by sea rise (Hardy, Jeffcoate & Dennis 2017). In an interesting paper, Tilley & Dennis (2017) discuss the probability of butterflies reaching an island (in this case using Flat Holm and Steep Holm islands in the Bristol Channel) from a shore-line population, simply by chance, and then finding an essential food resource there. It was found that there is a probability of several percent that a number of butterflies will make such a crossing and, having arrived, have a significant probability of locating a necessary resource such as a food plant.

the presence of which allowed the dispersal of small mammals into the UK); the pattern of single colonisation is possibly explained by its relatively low dispersal capability (Combe *et al.* 2016).

Recolonisation may have been by direct routes (e.g. from France to southern England), as is surmised for the Meadow Brown (Schmitt, Röber & Seitz 2005), or by circuitous routes as has been shown for a wide range of fauna, including amphibians (Snell, Tetteh & Evans 2005) and beetles (Bilton 1994). There is apparently a general reduction in genetic diversity and the number of subspecies northwards from southern to northern Europe, due to rapid expansion northwards after ice retreat and the varied topography of southern refugia which allowed populations to diverge through several ice ages. The Adder is a typical example; Ursenbacher *et al.* (2015) found a reduction in genetic diversity from the core of the distribution to peripheral populations[68] with separate isolated postglacial recolonisation from glacial refugia in south-west and central France, in permafrost-free areas during the last glacial maximum. Adder populations further from these glacial refugia had lower genetic diversity and reduced connectivity.

Beirne (1947) suggested that in the ice ages many species retreated to low-lying land now covered by sea but exposed as sea levels dropped. This theory has the benefit of fitting in with the coastal distribution of the various species such as the Sandhill Rustic moth (with populations in Cornwall, Lancashire, north Wales and south-west Ireland (Spalding 2015)) and the Kerry Slug (suggested as having survived the last glaciation in a mild refuge near southern Ireland (Forbes 1846, quoted in Beebee 2014)), but these theories of low-lying glacial refuges have generally been discounted on the basis that these areas would have been too cold to support most species (Dennis 1993). However, they were further south than modern tundra, the summer sun would have risen high in the sky and midday temperatures would have been much higher than on present-day tundra. Bhagwat & Willis (2008) suggest that some refugia were much further north than originally thought. St Dabeoc's Heath may have survived in a refuge on land now under the Bay of Biscay, from which it recolonised Ireland (Beatty & Provan 2013).

Key factors influencing the current distribution of species are generally the dispersal abilities of the species (Neve 2009) and the origins of the populations (Hewitt 1999). Scattered populations were probably linked to each other in recent post-glacial times; some of these populations might have become extinct leaving scattered relict populations behind, surviving to the present day, but leaving no sign of intervening populations and no clues as to the historic patterns of distribution. Alternatively, the current distribution might be evidence of multiple post-glacial colonisation events, colonies leap-frogging each other and arriving from separate founder populations. For example, several common species such as Badger (O'Meara *et al.* 2012) and Pygmy Shrew (McDevitt *et al.* 2011) found in Ireland are genetically different from the same species in Britain and this is probably due

---

68. This is called the central-marginal hypothesis (CMH).

Table 2.1. The changes in Britain's moth fauna since the last ice age[*]

Date	Changes in the fauna
13–14,000 yrs BP	Ice retreat and first climatic amelioration. First arrival of tundra species from south, followed by woodland species. Sequence of species of gradually more temperate climates.
10,500 yrs BP	Ice readvance. Retreat of southern species. Southern spread of northern species but no colonisation from north possible.
10–7000 yrs BP	Rapid climatic amelioration with forest closure to northern Scotland. Rapid recolonisation from south, latterly impeded by loss of land bridges. Forest species predominate. Upland and northern species retreat and become fragmented on isolated hills.
6000 yrs BP	Climactic optimum. Fauna includes many species now absent from Britain. Forest species predominate. Many northern and mountain species lost from Britain.
5500 yrs BP onwards	Climate slowly cools and becomes more oceanic. Loss of some "continental" species. Man's influence increases with forest reduction. Some restriction of forest species, extension of open ground species.
AD 1600–1830	Little Ice Age. Ice fields in Scotland, cold winters in England. Forest destruction reaches peak. Man's influence overtakes climate. Fragmentation of some species with use of western refugia. Loss of southern species. Some extension of northern species, but no gains from the north.
AD 1830–1940	Some recolonisation from south but man's influence on habitats paramount with loss of some species. Fauna similar to today.
1940–present	Climatic fluctuations and latterly warming. Some recolonisation but main influence is man's effect on habitats with some losses. Reality of warming and its effects still to be established[**].

[*]Taken with permission from Young, M.R. 1997. *The Natural History of Moths*. Poyser Natural History. London. [**]There has been considerable research since 1997 on the effects of climate change on particular species and we are beginning to realise how rapid some of the changes are.

to a wave of colonisation events with one population colonizing Ireland naturally overland via Britain, and then a subsequent wave replacing the original colonisers in Britain after Ireland became isolated (Martínková *et al.* 2007). The Water Vole is currently found throughout Britain but studies of their genetic make-up shows two distinct genetic clades clearly divided between England and Wales on the one hand and Scotland on the other, even though Water Voles would not recognise this distinction (Strachan & Moorhouse 2006); the voles that colonised England and Wales following the last ice age were from south east Europe whereas Scotland's voles appear to be descended from migrants from northern Iberia, with many having black fur rather than brown.

Advances in the use of DNA have led to greater understanding of the different recolonisation pathways since the last ice age and before, and the variation in different refugia for different species. In Britain recolonisation occurred after the last ice age since the island was too cold to support species. On the wider continent the situation is more complex (e.g. Dapporto *et al.* 2011) and modern patterns for some species can be traced back further than the last glacial period. Some species are monocentric sedentary species, others monocentric expansive species, others polycentric species occupying many different glacial refuges. For the burnet moths, for example, our present day sub-species are young, being post-glacial or products of the last glacial period, whilst the very distinct vicariant[69] species diverged during an earlier glacial period (781–126,000 years before present) (Hofmann & Tremewan 2017). It is generally accepted that there are three major faunal types resulting from different refugia and subsequent colonisation routes:

- Mediterranean elements with exclusive glacial survival in the Mediterranean refugia.
- Siberian elements with glacial refugia in the eastern Palearctic and only postglacial expansion to Europe.
- Arctic and/or alpine elements with large zonal distributions in the periglacial areas and postglacial retreat to the North and/or into the high mountain systems.

The clearwing moths (of which there are 116 species in Europe) appear to have recolonised Europe from both southern and eastern Europe, with species from Siberia having wider ranges than those of Mediterranean origin, and species feeding as larvae on/in wood being more widespread than other species (Ulrich *et al.* 2011).

However, genetic analysis has unravelled numerous additional refugia both of continental and Mediterranean species, thus strongly modifying the biogeographical view of Europe.[70] This modified notion is particularly true for the so-called Siberian species, which in many cases have not immigrated into Europe during the postglacial period, but most likely have survived the last, or even several glacial phases, in extra-Mediterranean refugia in some climatically favourable but geographically limited areas of southern Central and Eastern Europe. Recently, genetic analysis has revealed that typical Mediterranean species have also survived the Last Glacial Maximum in cryptic northern refugia (e.g. in the Carpathians or even north of the Alps) in addition to their Mediterranean refuge areas (Schmitt & Varga 2012).

For example, it is thought that the modern day distribution of the Mountain Ringlet depends on refugia patterns prior to the last glacial period as the genetic differentiation is too strong to support an exclusively post-glacial origin (Schmitt,

---

69. Vicariant: the separation or division of a group of organisms by a geographic barrier, such as a mountain or a body of water, resulting in differentiation of the original group into new varieties or species.

70. Different refugia may have been in place for non-European species. For example, it is considered that the high altitude areas of central Honshu in Japan functioned as interglacial refugia in far East Asia for many organisms of cold regions, including Lepidoptera (Nakatani, Usami & Itoh 2007).

Hewitt & Müller 2006). This butterfly is found in Britain and tends to go down into the vegetation when the sun gets too hot. Why did it not occur all over southern Europe during the colder glacial periods?[71] The most plausible explanation is that the rather dry and continental climate of European glacial steppes was most probably not suitable for a butterfly with such humidity demands.[72]

On the other hand, most cold resistant species were probably widely distributed during the last ice age with its cold and dry climatic conditions and only became disjunct after the climate warmed and their habitats shifted pole-wards and to higher elevations in mountains. For example, Scotch Burnet is currently found in three main regions (Hofmann & Tremewan 2017):

- An arctic sub-area in Scotland and the tundral regions of Finland, Norway, Sweden and parts of Russia.
- An alpine sub-area in separate regions of the high mountain ranges of southern Europe.
- A Siberian sub-area between Lake Balkash and Lake Baikal.

During the last ice age, a sub-arctic or periglacial zone existed from northern Spain and western France eastwards into modern-day Russia, where the Scotch Burnet would have been widely distributed. About 10,000 years ago it began to move northwards as far as Scotland and southern Scandinavia, with isolated populations with no chance of upward movement on mountains becoming extinct, but it was still widespread until about 8000 years ago when the climate warmed. Extinctions increased in the climatic optimum between 8000 and 5000 years ago when the tree line in the Alps shifted upwards by 200–300m higher than today. Expansions (in the cooler years between 5000 and 2500 years ago) and contractions (during the period of the Roman Empire, when Hannibal crossed the Alps with elephants) occurred until the present range was established. Southern mountains in Spain, Morocco and Greece were never reached as they were too far south from the periglacial zone. The genetic differentiation between populations on the Alps and Pyrenees is very weak[73] due to the recent separation and there are almost no significant characters for distinguishing European populations, not even the small isolated Scottish populations.[74] For species groups such as butterflies, spiders and

71. Schmitt, Hewitt & Müller (2006) found strong differentiation into five different lineages supporting five glacial centres: (i) the eastern Pyrenees, (ii) the mountain ranges between the central Pyrenees and south-western Alps, iii, iv) two areas along the southern Alps margin and (v) the northern Alps margin.
72. Genetic studies are not the answer to everything. It is important to know something about the ecology of a species – the Mountain Ringlet study demonstrates the explanatory value of combining genetic measures with knowledge of species physiology and life history (Schmitt, Hewitt & Müller 2006).
73. Post-glacial isolation in Alps and Pyrenees has resulted in a weak genetic differentiation between these two disjunct high mountain systems (Schmitt & Hewitt 2004).
74. Hofmann & Tremewan (2017) estimate that Scotch Burnet must have moved from north of the Alps to Scotland at an average speed of 250–400m per year. I have made several attempts to see this species; each year I have either been too early or too late; each year the weather has been bad when I have been up the mountain and good when I have come down. One year with Mark Young we walked

caddisflies, populations from adjoining high mountain systems often show similar genetic lineages, a phenomenon best explained by postglacial retreat to these mountains from one single differentiation centre between them (Schmitt 2009).

Mountain ranges are thought generally to have played a major role in the postglacial re-colonisation of western Europe, as described for Scotch Burnet. However, as always with wildlife, the situation can be complex. For the Pine Processionary Moth, there are two deeply divergent clades[75] but surprisingly, these were not separated by the Pyrenees (Rousselet *et al.* 2010); rather than acting as barriers to dispersal as would be expected, mountains appear to have served as refugia during the Pleistocene glaciations, and current distributions largely reflect expansion from these populations. The explanation for this unexpected conclusion might be because one clade moved upwards with mountain pines, whilst the other moved horizontally with the lowland pine species.

The recolonisation pathways since the last ice age have effects on the current genetics of species with the result that traces of species historical movements are still visible today. One example can be found in the structural blue colouration[76] of male Common Blue butterflies (Kertész *et al.* 2019). When investigating colour variation on specimens collected over 100 years from Europe and Asia, clear differences were found between the eastern and western groups with a transition zone in the Turkey region; these differences can be tentatively attributed to bottleneck effects[77] during glacial epochs over the last two million years. The blue colouration is frequently used by butterflies for sexual communication, so these differences may have an effect on mating behaviour. The blue colour is a sexual signalling colour so differences in colour would have affected mating choices between males and females; these differences would have become fixed over many years by these mating choices and males and females of the wrong colour would remain unmated. A similar distinction of western and eastern groups within Europe is found in the Chalkhill Blue, in which detailed genetic investigations revealed that as a consequence of postglacial range expansion, distinct western lineages and eastern lineages are found, separated by a contact zone from north-eastern Germany along the German–Czech border and throughout the eastern Alps, with mountain ranges between Bavaria and Bohemia providing a strong barrier to hybridisation between the two lineages (Kühne *et al.* 2017).

Some species can occur in unexpected localities, and this can be a natural event without the influence of man, a natural function of the ecology of the species.

---

up through a thunderstorm, hiding our metal handled nets from the lightning – we found nothing (the previous day the moths had been swarming over the Crowberry). On my last trip I did manage to find two larvae in the sunshine – but no adult moths.

75. A group of organisms believed to comprise the evolutionary descendants of a common ancestor.
76. The blue structural colour is much more stable than pigment-based wing patterns and therefore more constant and useful for scientific investigation.
77. A genetic bottleneck occurs when a population is greatly reduced in size, limiting the genetic diversity of the species.

Many years ago, when it was still permissible to do so, I climbed to the top of Uluru with my young son Trystan on my back. It had been a very wet season and I was amazed to find pools of water lying in the hollows as I moved away from the crowds. Looking into these pools I was even more amazed to find what looked like miniature horseshoe crabs – in fact these were the Shield Shrimp, which are frequent inhabitants of ephemeral waters in southern Australia (Williams & Busby 1991). The eggs of these historic looking creatures can survive for many years in dry conditions before hatching when they get wet again – in fact they probably need to be completely desiccated before they hatch. The drought-resistant eggs from dried-up pools are then carried by birds or the wind to dry hollows and hatch when the hollows fill with water, rapidly maturing to adulthood, each specimen only 7cm long. I wonder how many years these eggs laid dormant waiting for the rain to come?

We can call species with no connection to history *McDonald's* species, after the American burger chain. These are species which spring up in unlikely places, which have no real connection with the habitat or landscape in which they are found. They are ransom species, perhaps non-natives, migrants, adventives, deliberate introductions or accidental imports. McDonald's restaurants make no claims to be historically settled within the landscape, although occasionally they are situated in very old buildings – the restaurant in Shrewsbury was based in the town walls which date back to the 13th century, but was closed in 2017 when the leased expired and McDonald's said that it was no longer suited to their needs. Newly built, these restaurants mainly sit in modern retail developments on the edges of town with other fast food outlets, hotel chains and out-of-town shopping warehouses which look the same from Inverness to Truro, with no concessions to local architecture, historic landscapes or sense of place. A Common Blue of the wrong shade of blue will not get a mate in these areas. The Scarce Blackneck will not survive even though its foodplant is present. The Black Hairstreak would only be found if introduced by Man. The Cave Bear has long since gone from the area. The Irish Badger would not feel at home. A butterfly flapping against a window in a McDonald's is not the same as a butterfly flapping in its own historic habitat.

CHAPTER 3. NATIVE OR NON-NATIVE

The re-establishment of the Large Blue butterfly has been a great success. The butterfly died out in 1979, its last site being near Ashburton in Devon where it had hung on in what proved to be sub-optimal habitat where traditional farming methods had allowed it to survive. Its penultimate site in the Tidna Valley (where it was definitely last seen in 1973[78]) on the north Cornish coast was more suitable in many ways, but a combination of rabbit decline (due to myxomatosis), cessation of scrub burning (swaling) and a lack of grazing led to a heightened sward height and the consequent disappearance due to a cooling effect of the red ant *Myrmica sabuleti* on which the Large Blue caterpillars depend. Since then, under the guidance of Jeremy Thomas, subsequently with David Simcox, under the auspices of the Joint Committee for the Re-establishment of the Large Blue[79], the programme has been a soaring success. Large Blues have been re-introduced to – and naturally recolonised – a range of sites across south-west England. I have been immensely privileged to have been a part of this success story since the late 1980s, as a member and former Hon Secretary of the committee and lead on the potential re-introduction to the north Atlantic coasts of Cornwall and Devon. But – is the Large Blue a native species? The re-introduced ones came from Sweden. It certainly could not be considered native when first released at Site X in 1983[80], nor the following sites at Y (near to Site X), A, B, C and D (in the Poldens – at least I think they were as by this time nobody on the Committee knew which site was which and we had to revert to calling the sites by their names); the letters were used in an attempt to stop the general public knowing where the butterfly was flying. An amusing incident happened when a walker contacted Butterfly Conservation to say that he had seen a Large Blue on a site called Green Down in Somerset; the site is bisected by a public footpath. Butterfly Conservation denied the claim but of course it was true.

Several leading conservationists objected to large sums of money being spent on this butterfly, claiming it was a foreign species and the money could be better spent on native wildlife – such as beetles in particular. They had a point – but the work on the Large Blue benefited a range of species including plants (Pale-flowered Violet), reptiles (Adders), butterflies (High Brown Fritillary), beetles (Green Tiger beetle), bees (*Panurgus banksianus*) and bee-flies (Dotted Bee Fly).

Over the years the Large Blue has adapted to its new habitat, changing its phenology, coming out earlier than it used to in order to coincide with the early

---

78. Tony Archer-Lock thought he probably saw one in 1974.
79. The Committee when I joined it in 1987 was full of amateur naturalists, some of whom were experts in their field, others who probably attended at least partly for the good lunches we had and the afternoon field trip; nowadays, I am perhaps the only "amateur" left as I attend in a voluntary capacity and all others represent organisations such as the National Trust, Natural England, Somerset Wildlife Trust, Gloucestershire Wildlife Trust and the Royal Entomological Society. Jeremy Thomas chairs meetings; Dave Simcox and Sarah Meredith carry out the key survey work.
80. We called this Site X in an attempt at secrecy.

budding of the larval foodplant Wild Thyme and even feeding on Wild Marjoram in hotter places. It was added to the Wildlife and Countryside Act 1981 (as amended) in 2007. Is it a *bona fide* native? – the jury may be still out for some people and of course the introduced Large Blue is genetically distinct from the extinct native species – but for others, now it has colonised places on its own, surely we can claim it as native.

There is the question of native to where? As an ecological consultant I become exasperated when landscape architects plant the same mix of trees and shrubs in Kent as they do in Cornwall. The classic case is Field Maple, which is widespread across England but hardly goes into Cornwall at all (French, Murphy & Atkinson 1999), and so does not support a typical Cornish invertebrate fauna; it is out of place in Cornwall. So too those other species beloved of lazy landscape architects such as Hornbeam[81] (very rare in most of Cornwall apart from the south-east, and even here is likely to have been planted), Wayfaring Tree (absent from Cornwall) and Dogwood[82] (largely restricted to the extreme south-east corner of Cornwall), and even Guelder Rose, which is very rare in west Cornwall. Wild Service Tree is also planted but it mainly occurs in east Cornwall with outliers on the Lizard Peninsula. Sea Buckthorn is native in eastern England but often planted in Cornwall where it has become an invasive species on the sand dunes, crowding out native plants. Deptford Pink is considered native in some places, alien in others; many populations may have been short-lived (Robertson 2016) and it is difficult to distinguish native and alien populations in Britain (Preston, Pearmann & Dines 2002). It is protected under Schedule 8 of the Wildlife and Countryside Act 1981 (as amended) from intentional picking, uprooting or destruction, selling, offering for sale, possessing or transporting for the purpose of sale (live or dead, part or derivative).

On a national scale, Whitebeam is often used for planting schemes. Common Whitebeam is suitable for planting (although not in Cornwall where it is not native) but the situation is confused because there are ten alien species in Britain, the commonest of which is Swedish Whitebeam (Stace & Crawley 2015). Identification between Swedish and the native Common Whitebeam is difficult and Swedish Whitebeam has often been planted in error (although its common name should give the game away), e.g. along the Channel Tunnel Rail Link (now HS1) corridor in Kent as part of the extensive woodland planting schemes with over a million trees being planted[83]. It is particularly unsuitable here as the woodland plots were planted according to the target NVC (National Vegetation Communities)[84] and

81. It is native in Britain only in the south and south-east.
82. Native only in the extreme south-east of Cornwall; elsewhere it is not appropriate as a non-native and prefers alkaline soils, and therefore only suitable in the area around St Germans, Torpoint and Saltash.
83. Along with my son Dylan and colleagues Catriona and Jane, we counted the trees in 2004 as part of a woodland beat-up survey, surveying each of the 1147 planted woodland plots; the results are confidential.
84. The specifications for the planting of the habitat creation plots listed the native Common White-beam *Sorbus aria* agg.

the presence of Swedish Whitebeam introduced non-native genetic material into local populations as it can cross-pollinate with Rowan and Common Whitebeam. The Swedish Whitebeam hybrid *Sorbus x pinnatifida* auct. (*S. intermedia x S. aucuparia*) was also present. It was agreed that Swedish Whitebeam would be removed as part of the general management of the woodland plantings within the rail corridor where there were large aggregations. In line with good practice for habitat creation the stock that is used should be of local provenance and should not include certain species outside their natural distribution range.[85]

Swedish Whitebeam is classed as an alien, i.e. a species which has migrated to an area with human involvement (Stace & Crawley 2015). As we have seen in Chapter 2, wildlife was absent from the British Isles during the last Ice Age; alien species may have arrived here at any time (after Man recolonised Britain) from glacial refugia in what is now Spain and eastern Europe; by definition no alien species could have arrived before Man recolonised Britain. As a consequence, all species which arrived before man returned to Britain about 7–8000 years ago would be classed as non-alien, i.e. native. Stace & Crawley (*loc. cit.*) class a native plant as one that has originated in the area without human involvement or that has migrated to the area without human intervention from an area where it is or was native. They make no allowance for the time scale involved and they suggest that a new native plant could arrive tomorrow if brought here from a native area e.g. by a bird; so a newly arrived species would be classed as native if it arrives under its own steam. Others may not agree, especially those concerned with more mobile species than plants. "Native" to the ordinary man has links to birth and upbringing, and hence association with a certain place; for the biologist "native" implies a natural link with a particular habitat, and as such an adaptation that implies successful survival. No one seeing a Monarch butterfly on a Buddleia bush in the UK would claim that it was native.

The Amateur Entomologist Society's website defines indigenous in this way: an indigenous organism is an organism that is naturally occurring (i.e. has not been introduced by man) in a specific area. Indigenous organisms are sometimes called native. We can broadly classify species into three main types: native, non-native (alien) and immigrant. We can then sub-divide these into various sub-classes e.g. escape, feral, naturalised, established, re-established etc.

Good useable definitions are provided by Falk-Petersen, Bøhn & Sandlund (2006):

> **Native/indigenous/original:** An organism occurring within its natural past or present range and dispersal potential (organisms whose dispersal is independent of human intervention).

---

85. It is worth noting that some arboriculturalists promote planting non-native species in order to anticipate future climatic warming; this is not necessary as native trees in the UK can cope with increased temperatures as a natural part of their range.

Non-native/alien/adventive/exotic/foreign/introduced/non-indigenous/ novel: An organism occurring outside its natural past or present range and dispersal potential including any parts of the organism that might survive and subsequently reproduce (organisms the dispersal of which is caused by human action).

Immigrant: An organism that moves into a community or region where it was previously not found.

Other definitions include re-establishment. It is interesting to note that the Joint Committee for the Re-establishment of the Large Blue was originally (in 1963) named the Joint Committee for the Conservation of the Large Blue and then the Joint Committee for the Re-introduction of the Large Blue; re-establishment implies successful re-introduction particularly where the butterfly itself manages to recolonise former areas (after the original introduction).

At what historical point does a species change from being native to non-native? How long does it have to be here? Webb (1985) suggests that the key historical event is the arrival of man, i.e. those species present since prehistoric times are native – and to be native surely they need to still be here. If we exclude micro-species of brambles etc., Britain has about 1500 native species of higher plants (Thompson 2015). The last unambiguously native plant species to be found in the UK was the circumpolar Arctic-montane plant Iceland Purslane (Thompson 2015), found on Sky and Mull on bare, intermittently flushed or constantly moist, basaltic gravel pans and screes (Preston, Pearman & Dines 2002).

For alien non-native plants, the year 1500 is considered a key date. They can be divided into two main classes: archaeophytes and neophytes. Archaeophytes have been present in an area in a wild state since before 1500 and can be called "honorary natives" because they have been here so long (Stace & Crawley 2015). Neophytes are considered parvenus – they are alien plants which have only been here since 1500. Neophytes include naturalised or established plants and time is an important part of the concept of native and non-nativeness. In Cornwall, just over half the plants that have been recorded in the wild are non-natives – either archaeophytes or neophytes (French 2020). Native plants are the most common and widespread in Cornwall; out of the top 100 plants, ranked according to the total number of 1km squares in which they occur in Cornwall, only four are non-native plants – Sycamore, Pineapple Mayweed, Cut-leaved Crane's-bill and Montbretia.

There is no agreed alienation date for invertebrates. Dennis (1993) suggests that the Small Tortoiseshell and Peacock butterflies were established in Britain 13,000 years ago well before farming. Invertebrates may be more mobile than plants, especially long distant migrants such as the Painted Lady and the Monarch butterflies (as we shall see in Chapter 5) although the wind-blown seed of grasses for example can travel large distances (up to 21km for a genetically modified

Table 3.1. First British records or illustrations of resident British butterflies (not always by the name used today) (from *the Moths and Butterflies of Great Britain and Ireland* volume 7, 1991); *extinct in Britain since about 1925.

Species	Date
Chequered Skipper	1798
Small Skipper	1704
Essex Skipper	1889
Lulworth Skipper	1832
Silver-spotted Skipper	1803
Large Skipper	1704
Dingy Skipper	1666
Grizzled Skipper	1696
Swallowtail	c.1585
Wood White	1666
Brimstone	1634
Black-veined White*	1634
Large White	1634
Small White	1634
Green-veined White	1634
Orange-tip	1634
Green Hairstreak	1666
Brown Hairstreak	1703
Purple Hairstreak	1710
White-letter Hairstreak	1703
Black Hairstreak	1828
Small Copper	1699
Small Blue	1795
Silver-studded Blue	1775
Brown Argus	1704
Northern Brown Argus	1793
Common Blue	1634
Chalk Hill Blue	1704
Adonis Blue	1717
Holly Blue	1710
Large Blue	1795
Duke of Burgundy	1696 or earlier
White Admiral	1703
Purple Emperor	1704
Red Admiral	1634
Painted Lady	1634
Small Tortoiseshell	1634
Peacock	1634
Comma	1634 or 1710
Small Pearl-bordered Fritillary	1666
Pearl-bordered Fritillary	1699
High Brown Fritillary	1699
Dark Green Fritillary	1634
Silver-washed Fritillary	1699
Marsh Fritillary	1710
Glanville Fritillary	1703
Heath Fritillary	1699
Speckled Wood	1666
Wall	1634
Mountain Ringlet	1808
Scotch Argus	1760–1769
Marbled White	1666
Grayling	1699
Gatekeeper	1666
Meadow Brown	1666
Ringlet	1666
Small Heath	1666
Large Heath	1795

Creeping Bentgrass).[86] Early names and records for Lepidoptera show how long some species have been in Britain, but none are before 1500. James Petiver (1695) was the first to use vernacular names for British Lepidoptera[87] – Brimstone, Admiral (Red), Painted Lady, Peacock's Eye, Greater Tortoiseshell, Lesser Tortoiseshell, Comma. These gave rise to some of the first butterfly names as listed in Table 3.1. The oldest specifically-dated record in the National Moth Recording Scheme is currently a larval field record of Scarlet Tiger from London, Greenwich (Charlton), West Kent (VC16), by Mr James Dutfield on 20 April 1746. Benjamin Wilkes (1747–1749) records that the Kentish Glory was found near Westerham Kent. Moses Harris (1775) refers to Cream-spot Tiger, Nettle-tap and Pale Tussock. The first known records for Lepidoptera in Cornwall[88] are the Silver-washed Fritillary and Purple Hairstreak by Colonel G. Montagu in 1796 and Brimstone by the same person in 1797. The first moth record for Cornwall is for Convolvulus Hawk-moth some time before 1834, flying onto a fishing boat, knocking itself out before flying off again when it had recovered. Later records include Marbled Clover (1840), Feathered Ranunculus and the micro-moth *Phyllonorycter spinicolella* (both 1844). Ironically the oldest pinned insect in the world is probably a Bath White captured by William Vernon in Cambridge in May 1702; Bath Whites are not resident in Britain! The oldest known insect collection is that of English botanist Leonard Plukenet (1641–1706) who pressed his insects between the pages of a book like botanical specimens; butterflies included the Small Tortoiseshell, Peacock and Meadow Brown. Sir Joseph Banks (1743–1820) and Sir Hans Sloane (1660–1773) collected butterflies and these collections are still in the Natural History Museum, London.

The micro-moth *Aethes rutilana*, which used to be found in south-east England, has been recorded feeding on prostrate Juniper in hot areas on south-facing slopes in western Scotland. It probably colonised Scotland in a warmer period perhaps over 5000 years ago, and intermediate populations disappeared during subsequent cold periods; in this case the micro-moth would be considered as native. Those moth species that are confined to northern Britain may have been present for longer than those in the south, as these northern moths are more likely to have been early colonisers, having arrived during cool post-glacial periods before more warmth-loving species followed from continental Europe into southern England (Table 3.2). These include the grass moth *Crambus furcatellus*, Broad-bordered White Underwing and the Black Mountain Moth.[89] The leaf-miner *Stigmella dryadella* is

86. *New Scientist* 20 September 2004.
87. Earlier books, e.g. by Wooton and Mouffet, figured butterflies but none is given a name.
88. From ERICA = Environmental Records in Cornwall Automated, which is a species database prepared by Colin French for the Cornish Biological Records Unit and now supported by him as a service to all species recorders in Cornwall and the Isles of Scilly. It is a magnificent achievement and a real contribution to the understanding of the region's changing wildlife.
89. I searched for Black Mountain Moth on the Cairngorms with my great friend Steve Church. We went up in the chair lift, which is a frightening experience as it swayed around in the wind. Steve was unhappy with the experience but the moth prize was too great to resist. At the top we were in thick fog, so we spent the day in the café, looking out of the window as the cloud swirled around us. When the café closed, we trudged down the supply road, and I saw a single Black Mountain Moth on the

likely to have been an early coloniser and a definite British native. The caterpillars at low altitudes feed on the coast on Mountain Avens in the north of Scotland, but high above sea level further south in the Scottish Highlands (Young 1997); Mountain Avens is found recorded from sea level in west Sutherland and the Burren (Co. Clare) up to 1035 m on Ben Avon in Banffshire (Preston, Pearmann & Dines 2002).

Table 3.2. Examples of sub-arctic moth species (based on Ford 1972).

Northern Arches
Small Dark Yellow Underwing
Broad-bordered White Underwing
Netted Mountain Moth
Northern Dart
Black Mountain Moth
Slender-striped Rufous
Mountain Burnet
Cousin German
Grey Mountain Carpet
Yellow-ringed Carpet
Manchester Treble-bar

Of course, we may not know how long a species has been here. The Small-flowered Tongue Orchid was first recorded in Britain in 1989, near Penlee Point in the extreme south-east of Cornwall. I went to see it in 1990. It had been protected from damage by wire netting but the area around it had been trampled as photographers had removed the wire netting so that they could take good photos. Was it native? Some thought it was planted deliberately but Steve Madge thought it had arrived on wind-blown seed (Madge 1999). Orchids have minute seeds – like dust; you can get up to 45,000 Common Spotted Orchid seeds into a teaspoon (Morgan 2019). The fact that it was discovered after the gorse scrub was cleared for a fence line suggests that it had been there for many years, but hidden from plant hunters by scrub. The flowers are small and inconspicuous and it could have been easily overlooked; it can self-pollinate. It has also been recorded from Brittany. These facts taken together suggest that it is likely to be native[90], although in an interesting but necessarily inconclusive article Morgan (2019) implies that the frequency in recent years of European orchid arrivals in Britain such as the Small-flowered Tongue Orchid suggest the agency of humans. If native, many people would consider that its conservation value is now very high and it becomes worth spending time and money conserving it.

---

way down as we descended into sunlight. I failed to catch it. At the bottom we looked up and saw that the clouds had cleared and the plateau was in bright sunlight. We trudged back up again (the chair lift was closed) and criss-crossed the clittery summit searching the Crowberry foodplant without success.
90. Note that after it was discovered some material was taken, propagated and replanted; the last plant was seen in 2008 and this might have been a planted one (Stace & Crawley 2015).

The Purple Tiger moth is an interesting example. It has only ever been recorded once in the UK. A typical preserved male set on a 30mm steel pin was discovered in a collection in 1983 (Pratt 2020). It had been anonymously labelled by hand as being captured at Hove Carlisle Road in July 1910; this road runs north–south and the southern part is just 100m from the sea. This species is widely established in Europe, the larvae feeding on low-growing plants, and I have often caught it myself in moth traps abroad. However, the close proximity of the site to "a high density of dealers in lepidopterous specimens immediately throws suspicion over its authenticity" (Pratt 2020). Pratt goes on to suggest that this species was not amongst the dealers' regular wares and "skepticism over its source is just outweighed by the detailed labelling." Some dealers were notorious fraudsters.

The Lunar Double-stripe is a rare migrant to the UK, but at one time was resident. Pratt (2020) tells the story of a specimen caught by M.S. Blaker on a sugaring expedition[91] near Lewes on 17th June 1873; the named locality was deliberately misleading to prevent dealers rushing there and collecting all the specimens. Blaker was alarmed to hear that his specimen was for sale in an auction catalogue. Thinking he had been robbed he checked his moth cabinet and found his moth still there, so he went to the auction and found a foreign moth with a complete copy of his own label. Native specimens of Lunar Double-stripe could fetch as much as £5, equivalent to £250 today.

Even when we know how long a species has been here, we might not know whether it is native or not. Bermuda Grass has been known in the British Isles since it was recorded in Cornwall by Mr J. Newton as plentiful between Penzance and Marazion in Cornwall; it is still there in abundance. It has since been found in Cornwall in other places, but in these places – and elsewhere in Britain – it is likely to have been planted as part of a grass mix; it is very tough and resilient so suitable for areas where heavy trampling is predicted. It is generally considered as of uncertain status (Stace & Crawley 2015). In 2012 my friend and colleague Catriona Neil recorded this plant for the first time in Scotland on a beach on the Dumfries and Galloway coast whilst looking for Sandhill Rustic moths; it was a long way from any habitation and definitely not planted. She submitted the record for publication in *Watsonia* but the editor thought it of little interest and declined to publish – although many people would have been interested. I would consider that it was either native or a natural colonisation.

The Pine-tree Lappet moth was first recorded by Dougie Robinson in a moth trap in Inverness on 29th July 2004 and was assumed to be a migrant from the Continent; it had previously been recorded in southern England (Prescott 2017). Then in 2007 two males were caught in the Beauly valley near Inverness, with six more in 2008, and it began to be realised that it could be a breeding population. As such it could

91. Sugaring for moths is a method using a mix of rum, brown sugar and black treacle, boiled up to form a thick liquid, painted onto tree trunks or wooden fence posts; at night moths come to feed on the scented sweet mixture; this method has been partly replaced by wine ropes – natural fibre boiled up with red wine and sugar and laid across branches to the same effect.

be a potential threat to the forests of Scotland since on the Continent it is a pest species, being a major defoliator of Scots Pine. By 2013 it was confirmed that there was a low density population in the Beauly valley. The Forestry Commission established the Pine-tree Lappet Outbreak Management Team to find out where it was and formulate measures to stop it becoming permanently established. Restrictions were placed on timber movement to prevent its spread. The area around key Caledonian forests were monitored using pheromone traps in over 40 sites, sticky glue bands were placed on over 1000 trees to catch larvae descending to pupate and light traps were used to record and collect adult moths. They were helped in this by the charity Butterfly Conservation. But how long had it been there? – and if it had been there a long time, was it native and if so, how could it be classed as a pest species? It might in fact be a key part of the Caledonian forest ecology. DNA studies showed that that the Scottish population was unique. Based on the DNA there are three distinct groups. The Scottish group is genetically related to an eastern France to western Turkey group which suggests that there was a pathway from France during post-glacial times when Britain was still connected to Europe by a land bridge; the moth would have reached Scotland through ancient English pine woods which have now disappeared from England, and the moth disappeared with them. So, is it native or a non-native? If it is native it can be considered a rare species that needs to be conserved; if non-native perhaps it should be wiped out as a potential pest. At the time of writing the jury is still out, but the Pine-tree Lappet Outbreak Management Team continue to monitor the population in a precautionary approach, prepare containment plans (e.g. using pheromones to disrupt mating behaviour) just in case and eradicate it from woodland sites where it has not previously been found.

In the British and Irish collection of Lepidoptera in the Natural History Museum in London are two specimens in the series of the moth *Euzophera cinerosella* which looked out of place and they were dissected and found to be *Euzophera costivittella,* a moth which occurs in southern Russia, Iran, West Turkistan and Afghanistan (Agassiz 2017). One of the specimens of *E. costivittella* is labelled 'Torcross, Z. 1885' and the other is labelled 'Farn coll No.37698', and also 'Rait-Smith collection', but there are no other data. The two specimens would appear to have been collected and set by an English entomologist, since the style accords precisely with others taken at a similar time. They could not have migrated here (it is too far); they could have been purchased but they appear to have been set by an Englishman; their location and date of capture could have been mislabelled by mistake, but this is considered unlikely. They could have been the result of deception, which was sometimes practised in Victorian times so that exotic species could be claimed as British and as a result become more valuable, but since they were not recognised until now as being a different species there is no reason to suspect foul play. They could have been accidentally introduced along with imported host-plants; in the second half of the 19th century Torcross was developed as a tourist location, so we can speculate that the gardens here were stocked with some imported plants. After such an interval of time Agassiz (*loc. cit.*) suggests that

Table 3.3. The use of plant criteria for nativeness for moths and butterflies (from Preston, Pearmann & Dines 2002).

Native criteria for plants	Can these criteria be used for moths and butterflies?
Distribution in Europe is relatively stable	Rapid climate change has made insect distributions less stable than previously. Nevertheless stable core distributions may indicate long-term residence.
Distribution in our area is more or less continuous, or if not then reflects the similarly discontinuous pattern of suitable habitats	Disjunct distributions of many species make this difficult; it may be that a disjunct distribution may in some cases indicate long residency, e.g. where isolated populations are relicts of once widespread distributions now lost due to climate fluctuations. A classic example of this is the Sandhill Rustic moth, which occurs on the coastal fringes of Britain and Ireland in widely separated colonies (Spalding 2015).
Distribution in our area is a natural extension of the world range	This criterion works well for many insects, even those where the distribution in Britain is fragmented e.g. Scarce Blackneck. This may not work so well for species in south-east Britain where extension of range from northern France may indicate recent colonisation e.g. Toadflax Brocade, Fiery Clearwing, Scarce Chocolate-tip.
Distribution in our area has reached equilibrium and changes only in response to environmental factors	Patterns of moth distributions seem to change every year, these populations being less stable than plants which can survive in the same place for centuries e.g. Red Fescue which survives in clonal form for about 1000 years near Midlothian (Harberd 1961). The micro-moth *Agonopterix heracliana* occurs throughout Britain, including the main Scottish islands (Young 1997) and should be considered native.
Usually occurs in natural or semi-natural habitats	Native butterflies and moths are more likely to occur in natural or semi-natural habitats, although there are occasional reports of caterpillars feeding on non-native plants; Argent & Sable (Mcilveen 2015) and Elephant Hawk-moth caterpillars (Sproul 2015) have been found on Himalayan Balsam*.
Present in specific areas for long periods	Native butterflies and moths are likely to occur in specific areas for long periods. Northern species may be more likely to be present in the UK for longer than southern species, which may be more recent arrivals after the last Ice Age e.g. the micro-moths *Aethes rutilana* and *Stigmella dryadella*.
Recorded, or likely to have been present, before 1700 CE	I can find no detailed records of moths prior to 1700, although there are 32 butterflies**.
Continuous fossil record since glaciation	Butterflies and moths are rarely recorded in the fossil record. The earliest fossil reliably identified as a member of the Lepidoptera is *Archaeolepis mane* Whalley, found by J.F. Jackson of Charmouth in a Lower Jurassic calcareous flatstone deposit in Dorset, about 190 million-years-old; its wings are characteristically similar to those found in the caddisflies. *Archaeolepis* is not from an extant family.
*Himalayan Balsam was introduced as an ornamental garden plant in 1839 and was first recorded in the wild in 1855 (Preston, Pearmann & Dines 2002). **Perhaps we need a later date for moths – say 1800 or even 1900.	

we cannot be certain enough to claim that these two specimens count as British, but it remains a probability that they were taken in the wild in this country.

Preston, Pearmann & Dines (2002) provide a list of eight criteria for accepting native status; as an exercise I have considered whether these are suitable for butterflies and moths (Table 3.3). Most of these work for other insects as well although, as we have seen (Chapter 2), insects with hard chitinous wing cases such as beetles can be found in the fossil record; rapid climate change has also made insect distributions less stable than previously.

These criteria do not work for the Horrid Ground Weaver spider. First discovered new to science at Shapters Field Quarry, Cattedown, Plymouth by R.A. Stevens as recently as 1989 (Merrett & Stevens 1995), it is the only member of the genus *Nothophantes*. It has only been found at three sites, all of which are in Plymouth in or adjacent to limestone quarries where it can be found under rocks, in leaf litter and under human rubbish including discarded carpets.[92] Observations made since 2015 have shown that the adult spiders can be found between November and January with a peak around mid-December. Females kept in captivity have constructed egg cocoons between January and March. The adults die off at this time and the new generation emerges in April. The spiderlings develop over the summer and early autumn with the first adults appearing in October. At the time of writing (2020) only 145 individuals have ever been recorded and this spider is listed by the International Union for Conservation of Nature (IUCN) as Critically Endangered and included in Section 41: Species of Principle Importance in England (Natural Environment and Rural Communities (NERC) Act 2006. Plymouth is the only place in the world that it has been found. Is it native, overlooked because is so small? – or is it a recent arrival on ships, being found just 150m from the Plymouth docks. If so, where did it come from?

The history of some species is difficult to understand. The Belted Beauty is restricted in Britain to the west coasts of Scotland and north Wales (it is also in Ireland), although on continental Europe it is widespread in central Europe east to the Russian Urals. It cannot be a recent arrival as the female is wingless and too heavy to be carried by the male during mating. Yet it is common in the Hebrides. Flightlessness could not have evolved recently as a consequence of isolation here as it is flightless in continental Europe as well. Young (1997) suggests that the females managed to disperse across the sea on floating debris or even on boats, but if so it is difficult to understand how it spread across so many islands. Although Young discounts this, I would suggest that Belted Beauty followed the retreating ice after the ice age and reached these islands before they became isolated by rising water levels. If so, Belted Beauty would have been one of the earliest arrivals, with one of the best claims for native status.

---

92. My colleague Amy Horn-Norris surveyed for this species with expert John Walters in 2020 for a planning application. They did not find any.

The Pool Frog is an interesting case. It was found in Norfolk but considered as the introduced Edible Frog (introduced perhaps by Italian monks) until 1884, when it was correctly identified as the Pool Frog; however, it was still considered an introduced non-native species (Snell 2016). There is an introduced French population in Surrey. In 2005, genetic analysis indicated that the Pool Frog is native in Norfolk, well separated from the French populations and the introduced population in Surrey and closest to populations in Norway and Sweden; Norfolk and Scandinavian Pool Frogs have similar call accents. The Pool Frogs of Scandinavia and Norfolk also differ from their southern relatives in that their backs are darker and they bask at every opportunity, useful behaviour in high latitudes and cloudy climates. In addition, subfossil evidence of Pool Frogs was found from about 1000 years ago, demonstrating that the species occurred in the UK prior to known introductions; taken together, the evidence for the native status of the Pool Frog is compelling (Beebee et al. 2005). Unfortunately the Pool Frog had died out in 1995. A re-introduction strategy was prepared, with releases between 2005 and 2008 in Norfolk and then to Thompson Common in Norfolk using stock from the successful introduced populations. These Pool Frogs were added in 2011 to the Wildlife and Countryside Act 1981 (as amended) and became legally protected. But not so the introduced Pool Frogs in Surrey. Thus Pool Frog is listed[93] twice – as a native British species and as an alien species. The unauthorised French frogs are treated by Natural England as "of no conservation importance", even "though hardly anyone (and certainly not the frogs themselves) could tell (them) apart" (Thompson 2015). Perhaps they should be returned to France, now that Brexit has happened.

A species welcomed in one area may be unwelcome in another, like a President Trump in the House of Commons. This is shown by attitudes to creatures such as the Golden Jackal. Golden Jackals look like small grey wolves and will attack farm animals such as turkeys and lambs as well as small wild game like hares and pheasants, partridges and waterfowl. They have undergone a large-scale return throughout eastern and western Europe, which has been attributed to historical decreases of wolf populations[94] combined with a warmer climate due to climate change. The largest European population is in Bulgaria, and they are also present in Hungary, Serbia, Croatia, Slovenia, Ukraine, France and Italy, and they are expanding towards Central Europe. More recently, an isolated population was confirmed in western Estonia, much further north than their common range, and Golden Jackals were seen on camera traps in Germany on the Baltic Sea and in the Netherlands. A road-killed Golden Jackal was reported in Denmark. In some areas, they are seen as historic indicators of a former fauna, in other areas as signs of the great mix-up of wildlife to create a bastard faunal assemblage – or more simply perhaps as animals dangerous to farm stock, domestic pets and small children. What happens if a species is protected in one area but not in another?

93. http://www.herpetofauna.co.uk/identification.asp
94. The first Grey Wolf seen in Belgium in January 2018, the first for 100 years, disappeared in autumn 2019, probably shot, leaving a lonely male. The last recorded instance of a wolf being killed by a hunter in Belgium was in 1897 (Daily Telegraph 1 October 2019).

Trouwborst, Krofel & Linnell (2015) considered these implications. Golden Jackals in Europe are covered, either specifically or indirectly, by multiple international legal instruments, including the 1992 Convention on Biological Diversity, the 1979 Convention on the Conservation of European Wildlife and Natural Habitats (Bern Convention) and the 1992 European Union (EU) Directive 92/43 on the Conservation of Natural Habitats and of Wild Fauna and Flora (Habitats Directive), under which the Golden Jackal is a 'species of Community interest.' They are not listed under the 1973 Convention on International Trade in Endangered Species of Wild Fauna and Flora (CITES) or the 1979 Convention on the Conservation of Migratory Species of Wild Animals. The Standing Committee of the Bern Convention interpreted the term 'alien species' as 'not including native species naturally extending their range in response to climate change'. We should be welcoming rather than deterring species naturally changing their distribution in apparent response to climate change. Subfossil records denote Golden Jackal presence in parts of Europe for thousands of years. Trouwborst, Krofel & Linnell (2015) consider that the contours of a species' 'natural range' should not be determined top-down by member states' authorities but bottom-up by the animals themselves. They suggest that all EU member states where Golden Jackals occur, including countries where Jackals have recently arrived without human assistance, are bound by the Directive's obligations. In some countries such as Albania, Germany, Italy, FYR Macedonia, Poland and Switzerland the Golden Jackal is legally protected. Despite this, the governments of Estonia and Latvia regarded the species as alien (even though they probably arrived there under their own steam) and allowed unlimited lethal removal with the aim of eradicating the species, which resulted in several animals being shot in 2013 and 2014.

It is a well-established idea that being native is better in one sense – a native species is more fully established in the ecological community and has links with a greater number of other species than a new arrival. For example, the number of insect species associated with a tree is a reflection of the cumulative abundance of that tree in the particular country throughout recent geological history (Southwood 1961) so that the dominant native trees will have most insect species, and recently introduced ones fewest. Similarly, in Denmark beetle diversity is higher in hedges with native hawthorn than with non-native rowan and spruce (Lövei & Magura 2017); this is due to the presence of forest specialist beetles, tree root systems and fungal associations which are crucial for some soil-dwelling beetle larvae.

This concept is true of smaller plants as well. Blunt, Shaw & Shaw (2017) showed that Small Nettle, which is an archaeophyte, introduced here accompanying the spread of agriculture across Europe before 1500, supports fewer butterflies and moths than Common Nettle. Small Nettle provides food for the caterpillars of Red Admiral, Peacock, Small Tortoiseshell, Silver Y and Pearly Underwing, all being migratory or mobile species. In comparison, Emmet (1991) lists 20 species on Common Nettle: Beautiful Golden Y, Bloxworth Snout, Burnished Brass, Comma, Dark Spectacle, Frosted Orange, Jersey Tiger, Mother of Pearl, Mottled

Rustic, Nettle-tap, Painted Lady, Peacock, Plain Golden Y, Red Admiral, Setaceous Hebrew Character, Small Fanfoot, Small Magpie, Small Tortoiseshell, Snout, Spectacle. Common Nettle was present here in Britain in the Middle Pliocene, about three million years ago.

However, Alexander, Green & Morris (2016) called for a fresh perspective on the role of naturalised trees. They say quite correctly that it is a matter of perception rather than strict science whether one accepts non-natives and recognises their contribution to our biodiversity, and this is the main theme of this book. They list a series of trees which they consider may have an important role in safeguarding certain elements of our wildlife, including Sycamore which was first recorded in the UK as a planted tree in 1578 and which ranks highly for invertebrate biomass production. Sycamore has been recorded in more than 75% of the 10×10 km squares in Britain (Stace & Crawley 2015). Another tree listed is Horse Chestnut, which was brought into England in the 17th century; Stace & Crawey (2015) call it "virtually useless" apart from its value as a specimen tree, but Alexander, Green & Morris (2016) suggest that it is important for its prolific sap runs (which have largely replaced the elm sap-runs which disappeared during elm disease), the development of rot holes in the scars left behind by dropped branches and for the range of fungi it supports. In the wrong places these trees can be a problem – but they may play an important role in the aftermath of devastation by new pathogens such Ash Die-back *Chalara* disease.

Carthey & Banks (2012) agree that arbitrary cut-off dates delineating native from alien species are not scientifically founded. They argue that the logical criterion for determining the native status of a long-term alien species must be once its native enemies are no longer naïve; the only objective criterion for deciding whether an introduced species has sufficiently integrated to be considered native must ultimately be the loss of novelty – that is, when native species recognise and respond effectively to the introduced enemy. As local enemies lose their naïveté and coexistence becomes possible, an introduced species must eventually become 'native'. The Dingo was introduced to Australia about 4000 years ago, yet some naturalists consider that it is not native there. Australia of course is a special case as it has been isolated as an island continent much longer than Britain and developed its own unique fauna. The Long-nosed Bandicoot is a marsupial native to Australia that often feeds at night in gardens. Carthey & Banks (2012) showed that they have learned to be wary of dogs even when kept inside at night and they suggest that this is because they recognised the threat posed by dogs based on thousands of years' experience with wild Dingoes, which are very closely related to domestic dogs; the Bandicoots were no longer thought to be naïve towards Dingoes, which should then be considered as native.

We all make assumptions as to the suitability of species to be here. The spectacular Clifden Nonpareil moth used to be resident in south-east England in Orlestone Woods from about 1935 to 1964; it may also have been resident in Norfolk. Since that time it has been a regular, if occasional, visitor as a migrant. I once saw several in my moth trap in central France, when trapping with my friend Bill Kittle, but we had to turn the lights off due to a huge swarm of hornets around the light and in the trap. Nineteen Clifden Nonpareil were recorded in Devon in 2018, Barry Henwood and Richard Fox reporting that "It is a welcome addition to our moth fauna" *(Devon Moth Group Annual Report 2018)*. In contrast, in the same report, Bob Heckford reports on nine records of Boxworm Moth as "the most significant addition to Devon, but not in a good way." The larvae are a serious pest of Box *Buxus* spp. in gardens, their defoliation sometimes killing the plants. Bob and I, with Stella Beavan, saw large infestations in Croatia. The assumptions are quite contrasting.

People want attractive, often rare species to be native, providing they are harmless (Thompson 2015). The Boxworm Moth fails this test; it is quite attractive as an adult moth, but the larvae are small, yellow and black, toxic and a serious pest (Plant *et al.* 2019). The Snake's Head Fritillary passes the test of beauty and rarity, but it is probably not native (Thompson 2015); Preston, Pearmann & Dines (2002) state that it has never been clear whether populations in traditionally managed floodplain meadows in central and south-east England are native. Despite this, it is a favourite plant for many. Everyone loves the Brown Hare[95] but not so with Rabbits; both were native before the last ice age, but then disappeared as the ice came. Rabbits were introduced by the Normans, firstly in warrens to provide food, then there was a substantial increase in wild populations from about 1750 due to changing agricultural practices and increased predator control to protect game (Harris & Yalden 2008); declines after the deliberate introduction of myxomatosis in 1953 have shown conservationists how important these animals are for nature conservation. Brown Hare may have been introduced from the Netherlands or Denmark during the last ice age, and were definitely present in Roman times (Harris & Yalden 2008). In contrast, the Mountain Hare is native, recorded from fossil evidence in England 12,600 to 12,950 years ago; probably once widespread, its range may have been reduced by the spread of woodland, or by competition with the larger Brown Hare or by the spread of people (Harris & Yalden 2008). Mountain Hares are probably even more popular than Brown Hare, perhaps due to their winter white colour change.

Our modern simplified understanding of native perhaps derives from H.G. Watson, a keen 19th century botanist who in 1852 devised the Watsonian vice-county system still in use today to define geographical boundaries for recording plants (it is now also used for recording moths and other species). Watson defined "native" as "apparently an aboriginal British species … no reason for supposing it to have been introduced by human agency" (Thompson 2015). However, he also accepted that long-established alien plants introduced by human agency were *de facto* natives and "constitute a part of the British flora, with just as much claim as

---

95. Although some people loved them so much they went hare coursing, which became illegal in England in 2005.

the descendants of Saxons or Normans have to be considered a part of the British nation." For recent arrivals, how much human agency is required to make a species an alien? Thompson (2015) points out that the world is physically and chemically transformed by man so that human agency is always present, for example making habitats suitable for alien species to colonise from continental Europe, such as the Tree Bumble-bee which was first recorded in Britain in 2001.

So are we to accept all species as equal, having equal right to be present in a particular place? Derek Ratcliffe in his 1977 *Nature Conservation Review* listed criteria for assessing the value of wildlife sites; although very useful at the time, these criteria are no longer used today in evaluating a site for which planning permission has been applied for. Under the "Naturalness" criteria Ratcliffe states: "An abundance or predominance of obviously introduced species usually, in fact, reduces the value of an area, though in moderation, non-indigenous species may add to diversity and interest." He then goes on to add: "Naturalness is perhaps of more concern to botanists than zoologists", a statement which probably says more about the state of nature conservation at the time than the difference between plants and animals.

Russell (2012), in answer to comments that the distinction between native and non-native species no longer holds value, states that the distinction between native and non-native remains as valid as ever. He defines invasive species as the subset of non-native species that cross a threshold for disproportionate negative impact in an ecosystem, recognizing that the majority of non-native species may have some positive – as well as negative – impacts (it is unlikely that all impacts of any invasive species will be negative). However, non-native species are the pathway to invasion and as such "Our ethical duty to non-native species, and to the invasive species that arise from them, therefore differs from our duty to native species. Because of this, the distinction between native and non-native remains as valid as ever. We must be pragmatic in our conservation decisions with limited resources, but we must not dress such pragmatism up as idealism and thus embrace invasive species in our native ecosystems."[96] Robertson (2016) takes an opposite view; he writes that "I do not think that the authenticity of wild plants, their otherness from the human-engineered environment, depends on native status."

Alien species hold a particular fascination for the public. When I was in Australia I bought a book entitled Australia's most dangerous animals. Forget the deadly spiders and snakes, one of the most dangerous animals illustrated was the European

---

96. The call to de-emphasise management of non-native species is related to a larger crusade that invokes an even stronger call to revise "traditional" conservation management practices. In the past decade, the "new conservation science" movement has sought to refocus conservation biology on protecting nature for services it provides to humans rather than on saving nature for its own sake (Doak *et al.* 2014). This view has led to the heralding of a new world order in which restoration ecologists will completely abandon the goal of returning an ecosystem to a semblance of its historical reference condition (Hobbs *et al.* 2006). This debate is beyond the scope of this book, which focuses instead on our valuation of species in their own right.

Wasp; seven deaths had been reported over a twenty-year period[97]; in the UK we might be mildly annoyed and knock them away from the jam jars at picnics. There is something more acceptable about a native poisonous species than an alien one. Nevertheless, many would think that it is too late to worry about such things. Thomas (2017) writes that the default stance of conservation to keep things as unchanged as possible and make the Earth "more natural" is untenable both because of the growing human population but also because it is not "obvious that the past state of the world is objectively preferable to the new state that is coming into existence."[98] He goes on to plea for a new relationship between humanity and the natural world in which humans are regarded as part of nature; this would imply no difference between the natural movement of species without the aid of Man (implying nativeness) and their unnatural movement (i.e. aided by Man). To him, Man has evolved but is still part of nature; the new distributions of species around the world are natural and "everything that we do to the rest of the world is natural." This seems to me to be a call to reject the historical and geographical context of individual species, a call to reject the biodiversity differences across the world, the *McDonaldisation* of our wildlife.

---

97. https://australianmuseum.net.au/learn/animals/insects/european-wasp

98. "Natural" is problematic in Britain because even pre-Neolithic vegetation had been radically altered by Mesolithic hunter-gatherers (Peterken 2019). Natural implies a situation in which there has been no modification by humans, but to some humans are part of nature; thus when describing forested habitats now we call it semi-natural woodland. Under this heading we can include future naturalness which would develop after man's influence was permanently removed, so that existing neglected woodland is moving towards a natural state. New woodland developing on cleared ground would be natural from the outset – even if it consisted of introduced but naturalised species such as Sycamore.

CHAPTER 4. THE ROLE OF MAN

We live in the Anthropocene. Everything is affected by Man, wildlife especially so. The Anthropocene was in full sway in Britain during the Industrial Revolution so perhaps the British are partly to blame for the loss of worldwide biodiversity, but it probably started with the extinction by humans of the megafauna in the Americas, Australia and New Zealand. Humans even probably got rid of the Neanderthals – after mating with them[99] (Kolbert 2014). Humans have become the "long-distance glue" that has converted separate continents into archipelagos of partially connected regions (Thomas 2017). Human dominance over nature has become so complete that we have altered almost everything whether we deliberately intervene or not (Rotherham 2014). All this despite a progressive decline in human–nature interaction (Soga & Gaston 2020) and the extinction of direct experience of wildlife for people, especially urban dwellers, where wildlife experience is via David Attenborough on the tv screen.

Wildlife can sometimes bite back, where there are negative interactions with nature such as snake bites, scorpion stings and attacks by large carnivores (Soga & Gaston 2020). The classic story of Moby Dick written by Herman Melville in 1851 – and made into a superb film 105 years later[100] – tells the story of Captain Ahab's quest for revenge against the great white Sperm Whale which took off one of his legs in his last whaling expedition. The Sperm Whale is followed, found and harpooned, but sinks the small whaling boats and the whaling ship Pequod itself. This is a story of obsession, but also of bravery by the ship's crew, and also of the unforgiven wild might of nature as expressed in the world's largest predator.

Nowadays, wildlife bites back at a smaller scale. This is especially so in developing countries, where poorer people tend to live in regions where there are more wildlife species that can cause them harm; in Mozambique there is a high incidence of crocodile attacks[101] associated with collecting water for drinking and catching fish (Dunham *et al.* 2010). In the early part of the 20th century, people in Africa were often killed by rhinoceros, buffalo, lion, hippopotamus and elephant – rhinoceros were considered by Theodore Roosevelt as too stupid to change their behaviour and hide from man, unlike the other dangerous species, so they stayed on the

---

99. My eldest son Dylan is 5% Neanderthal; I joke that it was probably from his mother's side, but then Neanderthal's had bigger brains!

100. Moby Dick was named after the white sperm whale Mocha Dick, one of the largest, most power-ful sperm whales ever reported, which destroyed more than 20 whaling ships and escaped another 80 before being killed, when it was found with over twenty harpoons in its back https://www.smithsoni-anmag.com/smart-news/real-life-whale-inspired-moby-dick-180965282/ accessed 8 April 2020. The film shows Right Whales being harpooned; the realistic filming hides the fact that model whales were used.

101. My wife Loveday and I were walking with my small son Trystan on my back on a beach north of Cairns with the sea on one side and a swamp on the other. As the sun started to go down we saw a thin line on the sand with indentations on either side. We began to think of salt water crocodiles emerg-ing from the swamp so we turned and went back. Walking a few hundred metres we saw the thin line expand into two lines, and we realised that the tracks were of a man wheeling a bike.

plains and being short-sighted were easy to shoot (Roosevelt 1909–1910). There were differences of opinion amongst the early game hunters as to which was the most dangerous animal – Roosevelt thought it was the charging lion: he shot one breaking its neck when it was just 100 yards away, writing "no finer sight could be imagined than that of this great maned lion as he charged … he (his son Kermit) could see all the muscles play as the lion galloped in, and then everything relax as he fell to the shock of my bullet."

White landowners in Africa keep the Big 5 game species – elephant, rhino, lion, leopard, buffalo – for shooting. John Hume has the world's largest rhino ranch where he breeds 200 rhinos every year to be shot[102]: "if it pays it stays!" – up to $350,000 to shoot a rhino, $50,000 for an elephant or lion, $20,000 for a leopard and $9,000 for a buffalo. This makes nature conservation economically viable, with nature as natural capital. The trophy hunters pay higher fees than the conventional tourists, so higher revenues come from fewer people with a lower environmental impact. Rhinos look deceptively docile; they can suddenly charge without any warning, when they sense your smell or hear your movement or when they finally see you with their tiny eyes. During my trip to South Africa we heard of a man who had his skull cracked by the huge jaws of a Hippopotamus so that his eye socket was displaced; the photos were horrific. But who owns the animals – the hunters or the animal rights activists – or the animals themselves?

Small things can also be dangerous. I was attacked by sand flies in Ecuador whilst moth trapping in cloud forest at Los Cedros nature reserve, and from the sand fly bites I was infected by leishmaniasis – maybe this experience is one of many that led me to my view of wildlife as fascinating but alien.

There is a view – eloquently expressed by Chris Thomas[103] (2017) – that change is good, that diversity has grown in nearly all regions of the world, there is an increasing variety of life, there are new opportunities for enterprising creatures, that Man is part of Nature, not separate from it, that the past state of the world is not preferable to the present and future state. In this world, human-induced climate change is a natural phenomenon, and we can observe how wild species move and adapt; in this world, it is good that the successful animals succeed. Thomas writes that it is time to "throw off the shackles of a pessimism-laden, loss-only view of the world." I sympathise with this view; it is a cold look at evolution in process, as some species survive and others go to the wall.[104] In this theme, we need to look at how Man attempts to control nature and plan the future, and in doing so re-interpret

102. *New Scientist* No 3160. 13 January 2018.
103. By chance Chris Thomas sailed around the Galapagos on the sister ship of the beautiful boat I was on in the early 1990s when joint leader for the Field Studies Council; his boat was called the *Diamante*, mine the *Andando*. I remember steering the boat as she sailed through a sea of phosphorescence under the Southern Star.
104. There are other views; the Prince of Wales, in his foreword to a book by Tony Juniper (2013) writes of our view of Nature: "A disturbing lack of a sense of the sacred – if nothing is sacred, most of all nature, then we create the potential for the perfect kind of storm…"

the past. Some of this control is deliberate, other influences are accidental, or by-products of actions. So, for sometime wild species, we:

- Exhibit
- Domesticate
- Allow to live with us (commensality)
- Alter
- Release – into the wild
- Introduce – deliberately or accidentally
- Eradicate – or attempt to do so
- Monitor
- Manage – often unsuccessfully
- Rewild

With each of these actions we express our view of wildlife as alien, as owned, as extensions of ourselves.

Exhibit

For many people, wild animals live in zoos or in television programmes. People own animals to show their wealth, prestige and dominance over wildlife. The boxer Mike Tyson bought three Bengal Tigers to parade both his wealth (they cost £144,000) and his power (he led them round on chains).[105] In Colombia the drug lord Pablo Escobar had a private zoo with (amongst other animals) twenty-four hippopotamuses; when he was shot and killed in 1993 the Colombian government took control of his estate, including his zoo. Twenty-four hippos escaped and have been thriving in the rivers around where he lived; with no predators and reproducing fast, by 2016 there were 35 hippos – the largest herd of hippos outside Africa.[106] By 2021 there were between 80 and 100 hippos and it is estimated the numbers could increase to nearly 1500 by 2040 if not controlled as the population is growing by 10% a year.[107]

Some zoos have a scientific purpose, others are there to make money, others still to make an impression. The first zoo was established by Queen Hatshepsut in 1500BC in Egypt by collecting animals from all over Africa and the Emperor Wen Wang of China built a zoo (named the Garden of Intelligence) to spread over 1500 acres with animals from all over his empire.[108] The Zoological Society of London opened the world's first scientific zoo to the public in 1847. Berger (2009) suggests that "Public zoos came into existence at the beginning of the period which was to see the disappearance of animals from daily life. The zoo … is a monument to the impossibility of such encounters." Now in a digital world we can see everything close-up and in colour, and the real actuality of animals may be unwelcome,

---

105. Tyson, M. 2013. *The Undisputed Truth. An Autobiography*. HarperSport.
106. *Daily Telegraph* 6 July 2016.
107. *Daily Telegraph* 18 January 2021.
108. https://timesofindia.indiatimes.com/Which-is-the-worlds-first-zoo/articleshow/1911504.cms?from=mdr

especially if they smell, do unseemly things to each other[109] and are behind bars. Nevertheless, some zoos are a joy to visit, especially where you can walk in a small rainforest amongst forest birds or creep through a room where bio-clocks have been reversed and nocturnal creatures walk and fly believing it is night during the day. Other zoos offer a desperate miserable existence. Quito Zoo on Avenida Amazonas when I visited it in 1987 was a sad place, full of unloved animals walking in circles on the concrete floors of their pens. As Berger (2009) writes: "You are looking at something that has been rendered absolutely marginal." The animals passively wait for things to happen to them; they have no control. "In principle, each cage is a frame round the animal inside it." The zoo was run by the military who seemed to have no interest in their captives; it was a relief when I found out the museum is now closed.

The exhibition of insects may be viewed differently, according to their reduced awareness and shorter life spans. They may be unaware that they are captive, and therefore still act as wild. There is no prestige in exhibiting butterflies and moths, no signs of power struggles to maintain control over them – not even the giant Black Witch or the White Witch that I saw in Brazil and Ecuador. Butterfly houses have been a great success with the public, where heliconid butterflies (e.g. the Postman) glide in front of children and adults photograph the nectaring butterflies a few inches from their faces (so that they have to move backwards to get the whole butterfly in the frame), and then pretend they spent hours struggling through dense thickets and swamps, braving leeches, to get the perfect photo. We can learn something from these captive butterflies, but perhaps not much about their natural choices in the wild.

I have a collection of moths. Not a complete collection of British Lepidoptera in a mahogany cabinet as some people do, laid out in taxonomic order, according to the numbers allotted by Bradley & Fletcher (1979), updated and renumbered by Agassiz, Beavan & Heckford (2013), with gaps of unseen uncollected specimens waiting to be filled, showing as white space in the moth drawer. In this way, the collector can take "a series", perhaps five of each species, and tell a story about each, each an adventure up and down the country, collecting at light by the moth trap or by day, killing and setting the specimens or perhaps collecting egg-laying females, from which they rear perfect specimens for the collection. The British Entomological and Natural History Society (BENHS) provides a home for many such collections[110] in cabinets at their headquarters in Dinton Pastures, Reading; even with the superb modern photography techniques, comparison with a collection is often the best way to confirm the identification of a difficult species. In contrast, my collection is haphazard, with lots of individuals of a few species. I probably have the largest collection of Sandhill Rustic moths anywhere in the world. In

109. A former colleague tells a story of a gull at Newquay Zoo which landed next to a resting lion, which leant over and gobbled it up, to the distress of a small child. Even in zoos, wildlife can be wild and real.

110. I was very proud to have helped in a small way in 2017 in the purchase by BENHS from his widow Jackie of the collection of the great entomologist Bernard Skinner.

this way, I can see small differences in colour forms and even sizes between populations; for example there are differences in wing area between males and females and between the different subspecies, some of which will fly more readily than others (Spalding 2013).

In the case of the Manchester Moth[111], a single specimen was prized so highly that it was exchanged for a collection of 2289 specimens of micro-Lepidoptera covering about 80 per cent of the species known at the time in the groups represented (Cook & McConville 2018). Why was the Manchester Moth so valuable? It was a combination of four things:

- It had been found only once in Britain – in 1829, on the River Irwell at Kersal Moor, north of Manchester where over 50 specimens were found on a rotting tree stump.

- The finder was Robert Cribb, a member of the Banksian Society, composed of "naturalists in humble life" or "ordinary mechanics". Little is known of his life; he gave three or four specimens away but afterwards refused to let any other specimens out of his possession because he was indignant that he was overlooked in the naming (the moth was named *woodiella* after R. Wood rather than *cribbiella* by the taxonomist John Curtis because it was Wood who sent it to him for examination).

- Cribb lost the rest when a pub landlady threw them on the fire when he didn't pay his debts. Only three specimens remained – two in the Manchester Museum, with a third specimen now in Australia.

- The man who desired this rare moth was the sixth Baron Walsingham, Member of Parliament and then the House of Lords, first class cricketeer, grouse shooter, world traveller, Fellow of the Royal Society, High Steward of Cambridge University, Trustee of the British Museum, editor of the *Entomologist's Monthly Magazine* (founded in 1864) and builder of a moth collection of over 260,000 specimens which he bequeathed to the Natural History Museum. As a man who was accustomed to shooting hummingbirds with dust shot to minimise damage to their skins, a major landowner and an expert on the micro-lepidoptera, he was not a man to give up on getting what he wanted. He gave his collection to the Natural History Museum, London in 1910, nine years before he died, but it was not until 1928 that the exchange of the Manchester Moth for the specimens in the Walsingham Collection at the Natural History Museum was completed.

Killing insects for collections is a contentious subject. The British Entomological and Natural History Society hold an annual exhibition in London at which

---

111. Now thought to be *Euclemensia schwarziella*, a north American moth that might have arrived in England in a consignment of bark, imported for use in tanning or dying.

entomologists exhibit dead specimens on pins, mostly those collected the previous year. Flies, beetles, bees, shieldbugs, caddis flies and ichneumon wasps are exhibited, but the most popular are the moths (foreign and British); butterfly exhibits used to be numerous but are less so now, perhaps partly because it can be difficult to find new things to exhibit, partly because it is rarely necessary to collect as an aid to identification or as confirmation of a find due to modern day digital photography but probably mainly because of a groundswell of opinion against collecting these beautiful creatures. It is of course okay to collect less obviously beautiful insects such as beetles and flies, although these can be incredibly lovely when viewed through a microscope. In 2017 David Ziggy Greene from *Private Eye* arrived and made sketches of the occasion for a cartoon. Some on the BENHS Council were worried that the published cartoon would be antagonistic to collectors, but it poked gentle sympathetic fun at the event (*Private Eye* No 1457).[112]

Domesticate
As I walked along a narrow footpath in Truro a middle-aged woman holding four whippets on leashes waited for me at the path end. As I passed her I thanked her for waiting for me, to which she replied, gesturing at the dogs "Oh, we're just waiting for their daddy." Dog people think of their pets as a special kind of wildlife, half human.[113] Juniper (2013) writes, "The upbeat feelings are especially enhanced if I have my dog. .... 30,000 years of canine domestication has not diminished her affinity with nature, either. Sniffing, listening and looking, she is utterly tuned in. In some ways we take walks in prehistory." On the other hand, the restless dog running through the nature reserve is viewed with alarm by real untamed wildlife, from the wading birds on the mudflats of Hayle Estuary in Cornwall where irresponsible dog owners used to set their dogs running across the shallow water for fun to see the birds rise and flock together – at least until 2008 when one individual was fined £250 plus £250 costs for disturbing the over-wintering birds – to the skylarks on Penhale Dunes where the number of territories increased from eight to 13 when people and dogs were excluded during the Foot and Mouth scare of 2001[114].

Dogs of course originated from the Eurasian Grey Wolf about 15,000 years ago in Central Asia (close to Mongolia and Nepal) and were the first domesticated species (Shannon *et al.* 2015).[115] Today they consist primarily of two specialised groups – a diverse set of nearly 400 pure breeds and a far more populous group of free-ranging animals adapted to a human commensal lifestyle (village dogs). Populations in the Neotropics and the South Pacific are almost completely derived from European stock, whereas other populations such as those of Vietnam, India,

---

112. I think I am figured in it as a figure leaning on a table and droning on about Victorian collectors.
113. As a cat lover, I have never been able to understand this view of dogs.
114. Spalding Associates (Environmental) Ltd. 2001. *Skylark Surveys at Penhale Dunes*. Truro.
115. Jack London (1906) wrote a novel about White Fang, the offspring of a she-wolf and a wolfish dog used to pull the sled – for White Fang "the law was Eat OR BE EATEN – the aim of life was meat. Life lived on life. There were the eaters and the eaten."

and Egypt show minimal evidence of European admixture. Dogs were kept because they were useful – some still are, of course, as guard dogs, police dogs, dogs for custom control, dogs for the partially sighted, company for the lonely. In contrast, the keeping of pets is largely a modern innovation. Berger (2009) expresses it well: "the pet is either sterilised or sexually isolated, extremely limited in its exercise, deprived of almost all animal contact, and fed with artificial foods … The pet offers its owner a mirror to a part that is otherwise never reflected … the autonomy of both parties has been lost … The parallelism of their separate lives has been destroyed." I know at least one dog owner who keeps his pet as a vegetarian.

These dogs are so far from real wildlife that many pure breeds are permanently damaged by inbreeding. The British Bulldog – first mentioned in 1632 – was used in bull baiting to latch onto a bull's nose and force it to the ground, with the first dog to do so the victor. Bull baiting became a national sport in England from the 13th to 18th centuries; the sport was abolished by an Act of Parliament in 1835. The Bulldog was kept alive by a few afficionados who bred them as companion dogs to become shorter-faced, squatter and more affable. British Bulldog health and well-being has been permanently damaged by inbreeding due to a dramatic reduction in the gene pool and it is possible that there is insufficient phenotypic and genotypic diversity to reverse these selection pressures to improve health and select against deleterious traits (Pedersen, Pooch & Liu 2016).

Domestication obviously changes animals in different ways. Dogs are capable of using gazing behaviour as a form of referential and intentional communication; horses not only look towards humans, but they are also sensitive to the attentional state of the experimenter. Even goats, which have been domesticated primarily for food rather than companionship, will gaze towards a forward-facing person earlier and for longer than an away-facing person and show more gaze alternations (Nawroth, Brett & McElliott 2016). In contrast, cats performed poorly in scientific tests and barely looked at humans, potentially owing to their rather solitary lifestyle. Many wild animals – such as Red Deer – will deliberately look away from humans.

Insects can also be domesticated. Fiona Presly found a wingless Large Earth Bumblebee queen in April 2017, fed her, kept her indoors, carried her to flowers, got her to drink sugary water from her finger, felt responsible for her wellbeing – the bumblebee never tried to sting her and felt anxious on another person's hand. She came to Fiona when she sensed she was there and spent a lot of time snuggled in her hand. She would crawl onto her nose and clean herself. When on Fiona's hand she would put her tail end off her hand to defecate. The bee "totally relaxed" with her. "We were both very comfortable with each other" Fiona claimed (Presly 2018).

As a boy in Kent I used to visit the Lullingstone Silk Farm near Eynsford in Kent; I can remember it well although I must have been less than eight-years-old, as it later moved to Hertfordshire. One attraction was the courtyard pool where you could scatter bread crumbs and watch the fish rise; another attraction was the Roman villa just along the road with its intricate mosaic floors. But as an eight-year-old I went to see the off-white caterpillars of the Silk Moth feeding on mulberry leaves. They had been domesticated for so many years that they did not need confining to their cage as they never strayed from their foodplant. The adult moths had wings but had forgotten how to fly; they stayed on their trays, where they mated and laid their eggs. The white cocoons were boiled to soften the silk, killing the pupae inside, and then the silk was reeled off in long threads, over the hot sweet smell of dead boiled cocoons. Each cocoon was claimed to produced 1/4 mile of silk. You could buy the larvae and take them home to feed on lettuce but they never survived, needing White Mulberry leaves to prosper. As a boy, I dreamed of making silk cloth to sell for shirts and ties. It is possible to take silk without killing the moths. In Madagascar silk is taken from the post-emergence[116] brownish cocoons of wild moths especially the endemic lasiocampid moth *Borocera cajani* for funerary silk shrouds (Cranston 2016).

Allow to live with us

Some animals seek us out to share our human habitation. Some we allow to live with us, the company of others we reject depending on our culture and personal foibles. Spiders looking for caves like to come into the house after it rains or for the winter; being an arachnophobe I close the windows when the autumn rains arrive so that I may sleep more soundly. Other people look on them as pets and welcome their rapid leggy advance across the carpet. Spiders share our table,[117] as it were, eating the flies that annoy us in the summer, in the sense of commensalism. Herring Gulls are synanthropes, benefiting from us as they feed on our waste tips and steal our chips as we sit on harbourside benches. Kinabalu Ground Squirrels search amongst waste baskets on the long steep stepped trail up Mount Kinabalu in Sabah.

One of the best known commensal animals is the House Mouse which shared our homes even before farming began about 15,000 years ago, at approximately the same time as dogs started being domesticated, displacing the Short-tailed Mouse. The change began before the advent of farming when hunter-gathers stopped constant roaming after wild animal game and formed longer term forager settlements. "Changing food webs and ecological dynamics in long-term settlements allowed house mice to establish durable commensal populations that expanded with human societies" (Weissbrod *et al.* 2017).[118] The House Mouse displaced the less commensal wild mouse during periods of heavy occupational

116. The fibre length is affected by the adult emergence hole so that for commercial use it is better to kill the pupae before the moths emerge. When the moths emerge they emit an alkaline fluid which softens the gum covering the threads causing the threads to become loosened so that they can be pushed aside by the emerging moth. This fluid leaves an indelible stain and rots the silk (Hart Dyke 1949).

117. Literally so in the Jatun Sacha nature reserve in Ecuador, where tarantulas used to hunt along the rafters above the trestle tables where we ate, occasionally dropping onto the table besides us as we breakfasted.

118. The story is told in changing molar shapes in mice from the Levant.

pressure but were outcompeted when humans moved around more often. The Short-tailed Mouse is associated with a seasonally mobile lifestyle; the House Mouse may have had the advantage in settlements because it could cope with a more flexible diet, had a greater stress tolerance and greater agility thanks to its longer tail.[119]

The clothes moths are well-known commensals – so well-known indeed that for many people all moths feed on clothes. There are five species regularly found in houses:[120]

- The Common Clothes Moth *Tineola bisseliella*
- The Case-bearing Clothes Moth *Tinea pellionella*
- The Large Pale Clothes Moth *Tinea pallescentella*
- The Brown House Moth *Hofmannophila pseudospretella*
- The White-shouldered House Moth *Endrosis sarcitrella*

The commonest of these is the Case-bearing Clothes Moth, which leaves little greyish larval cases on carpets and clothes – I lost a good suit to this species! The Common Clothes Moth can feed on imperfectly cleaned animal skeletons and probably spread with commerce throughout the world; it is now mainly found indoors. The Large Pale Clothes Moth feeds as a larva on keratinous animal matter such as hair, wool, fur or feathers, either indoors or out. All are poorly recorded by lepidopterists and are likely to be much more common than records indicate. They are members of the Tineidae family which feed as larvae on a range of materials including bird nests, hair, fur etc. – hence they can feed on carpets and clothes. I have seen huge numbers of tiny maggot-like tineid moth larvae feeding on the huge mounds of bat guano in the bat caves of Sabah and Sarawak, eloquently pictured by Harrison (1984). The Brown House Moth and the White-shouldered House Moth (members of the Oecophoridae family) are probably continuously brooded in warm conditions. The Brown House Moth gets its own back on moth collectors as it attacks moth specimens kept in poorly sealed collections. These species survive well in modern houses kept warm all winter by modern central-heating systems.

Alter

Now we can alter the very genetic structure of animals. The main target is for genetically modified (GM) crops so that we can feed Earth's burgeoning population. The general public are mainly against such interference with nature and the European Union have passed several directives and regulations controlling the cultivation, release and use of genetically modified organisms. A full consideration of agricultural GM technology is beyond the scope of this book and is a fast-changing world. The Oxitec Company can produce and distribute GM insects. They have changed the genes of Diamond-backed Moths so that they only produce

119. *New Scientist* 234: No 3119, 1 April 2017.
120. British Museum (Natural History) Economic Series No. 14. *Clothes moths and House Moths*. A 6th species listed in this book – the Tapestry Moth – is now rare, perhaps because it was always associated with unheated buildings before the introduction of central heating.

male offspring; releasing these into greenhouses caused populations of this pest-species of moth to crash.[121] The same company has created so-called Friendly™ Mosquitoes which are genetically engineered male mosquitoes which carry a self-limiting gene which, when passed on to their offspring, prevents them surviving to adulthood. These males are released to find and mate with wild females, passing on the self-limiting gene to their offspring and causing the population to crash. These self-limiting insects also contain a fluorescent marker gene which produces a protein throughout the body of the insect which glows when you shine a special light on it. This allows the company to monitor the offspring in the environment and adjust the location and rate of releases to achieve the best possible level of suppression – and of course with good business sense also provides the company with a steady source of income.

The technology spreads far beyond the world of crops. A research organisation in Japan has modified silkworms so that the silk proteins they make contain an artificial amino acid called AzPhe in place of a natural one called phenylalanine.[122] The modified silk protein can easily carry all kinds of molecules as a reliable reaction for attaching things, e.g. to bolt cells onto when growing organs for transplant. Silk proteins are important for medical use as they do not cause immune reactions in the body and are therefore suitable for scaffolds on which replacement organs can grow. A company in Singapore (Nanyang Technological College) has implanted electrodes into the flight muscles of male *Mecynorrhina torquata* beetles.[123] These Scarab beetles are amongst the largest flower beetles in the world, reaching 55–85mm long, and look like a larger version of the Rose Chafer found in the UK. With the implanted electrodes the bionic beetle can be steered left and right by administering small electric pulses; flight speed can be increased by increasing the frequency of the pulse. These modifications do not appear to reduce the beetles 3–6 month lifespan, but it is not clear whether the beetles are in pain. They are easy to control and cheap to obtain and modify and do not need batteries – but as adults they do need food (banana is good).

Release – into the wild

I have separated discussion of the release of animals from discussion of introductions (deliberate or accidental) as the former is carried out for sentimental or ceremonial reasons, often without an understanding of the released animal's ecology or survival requirements. There has, for example, been a large increase in the special event butterfly-release business, based on the release of butterflies such as Painted Lady, Monarch, Red Admiral and even Swallowtail, farmed especially for occasions such as weddings (John *et al.* 2015). These butterflies fly away and die, out of their natural habitat, many probably being eaten by birds almost immediately they are released. Painted Lady and Monarch, being strong-flying migrants, may survive for some time. It is now difficult to tell whether

121. *Daily Telegraph* 17 December 2018.
122. *New Scientist* 3172, 7 April 2018.
123. *New Scientist* 3177, 12 May 2018; see also Vo Doan & Sato 2016. More detail is provided at https://www.jove.com/video/54260/insect-machine-hybrid-system-remote-radio-control-freely-flying

sightings of Monarch butterflies are due to natural movement or wedding releases (Vane-Wright, Fage & Huertas 2017). There are several companies which provide butterflies for weddings, funerals and proms "to celebrate the emergence of a beautiful young lady after a journey of hard work and dedication – just like the Butterfly." [124]

The records of Emperor Moth and Poplar Hawk-moth on Fair Isle (Riddiford & Young 2017) are both of singletons found on cruise ships and released on Fair Isle as the first port of call, presumably in an act of kindness. Both moths were believed to have boarded the ship at some point between Leith and Fair Isle.

Wildlife activists release penned animals for sentimental reasons, and perhaps a misunderstanding of their ecology. American Mink, farmed for fur in the UK from 1929 onwards, escaped or were released from fur farms and led to self-sustaining feral populations in Devon by the late 1950s (Harris & Yalden 2008). Releases by animal rights activists increased in the 1990s; however these released farmed Mink were in effect domesticated and many were quickly caught. Mink had already colonised large areas of the UK by this time. Mink probably had a major adverse effect on populations of Water Vole as their arrival in some water catchments coincided with catastrophic Water Vole declines (Barreto *et al.* 1998) but the tide has turned and American Mink are in decline partly due to a recovery in Otter populations[125] and partly due to management by man (e.g. Bryce *et al.* 2011).

For a short time in my life, I farmed Red Deer in a wooded valley where the deer felt safe and where the hinds could hide their calves in wooded glades. They had abundant grass and I fed them kale, beet and nuts with molasses to keep them healthy and tame. (The cruellest way to keep Red Deer is in open grassy fields without shelter, unless perhaps they are born to these conditions). We had a bottle-fed calf, called no 47 from the tag in its ear, that used to run around in the kitchen on its spindly legs, slipping on the slate floor. The farm was surrounded by 2m high high-tensile deer fencing[126] to keep the deer inside. Some people unknown thought it cruel to keep deer and one night came down the valley, cut the fence at the furthest point from the house and carefully tied the fence back, leaving a stretch about 20m long open to rest of the world. On my regular walk around the perimeter fence I came aghast across this gap, thinking the deer would have all escaped. I then watched some deer walk along the existing fence line and then continue along the non-existent fence line, as though it was still there. I think, although it is impossible to be sure, that they knew they were safe inside the fence

---

124. *Butterflies for Occasions.*
125. Despite popular thinking, mink did not kill or displace Otter, which are larger and well able to look after themselves.
126. We were sold from New Zealand Cyclone fencing with 6-inch spacing between the risers. We did not know that this fencing was only suitable for internal fencing as calves could incredibly squeeze through the gaps; I once saw a calf outside the fence, thinking perhaps that the fence was broken, only to see the calf walk straight through the fence like a magic deer. Hurricane fencing was more suitable for the external fence, as the spacings were much smaller.

and that outside was danger – cars, people, poachers. Some time later I had a call from the RSPCA saying that someone had complained that the deer were kept in appalling conditions and he was going to come to check the farm. He came the same afternoon, saw the deer, saw the wooded glades, saw me call and feed them when they gathered round me, shrugged his shoulders and said that some people just objected when they didn't understand.

Introduce – deliberately

The natural landscape of the UK has changed enormously due to the deliberate or accidental introduction of non-native species. In Chapter 3 I discussed the meaning of native and non-native in the context of species arriving in the UK from abroad; the concept is not a simple one. In this chapter I discuss the introduction (deliberate or accidental) of non-native species by Man.

The practice of deliberate introductions emphasises the view of man that he is completely dominant over wildlife, which is either his plaything or his economic support. In 1826 the Zoological Society of London was formed at least partly "to introduce new and useful animals to Britain." In 1854, the Société Impériale d'Acclimatation was set up in Paris, followed in 1860 in the UK by the Society for the Acclimatisation of Animals, Birds, Fishes, Insects and Vegetables within the United Kingdom (the Acclimatisation Society): *it will be the endeavour of the Society to attempt to acclimatise and cultivate those animals, birds, etc., which will be useful and suitable to the park, the moorland, the plain, the woodland, the farm, the poultry-yard, as well as those which will increase the resources of our sea shores, rivers, ponds and gardens.* On 12th July 1862 a dinner was held which included on the menu the following exotic delicacies (Lever 1977): Japanese Sea Slug[127], Syrian pig, Pintail Duck, Kangaroo and Wild Boar ham, Tripang (sea cucumber) and Chinese yam. The Society gave up its exotic ghost in 1865 perhaps due to the over-optimistic ideas and claims of the Society members.[128]

There is a strong philosophical view argument against the introduction of non-native species. Jean-Jacques Rousseau, in exile from France and Switzerland, came to England in 1766 and volunteered to be plant collector or herborist for the Duchess of Portland – until she sent him the *Herbarium amboinense* (by Georg Rumpf), a catalogue of the plants of the island of Amboina (in modern-day Indonesia), published posthumously in 1741. Rousseau considered exotic botany to be the antithesis of the domination-free nature from which he derived solace and inspiration and objected strongly to the import of exotic plants as it "deforms nature" (Cook 2007).

---

127. I have eaten – or tried to eat – sea slug in Kuala Lumpur at a government dinner with the Minister for Tourism – I tried to spear it with a fork but it slithered off each time; the slug dish was on a circular spinning plate in the centre of the table and, with everyone watching and waiting for their turn, I gave up – and so have never eaten this delicacy.
128. A hoax Society report suggested that a member had crossed a Pintail duck with a rat, producing a hybrid of peculiar form and delicacy of flavour.

A variation on this is the practice of introducing mixes of plants that would never occur together in the wild, which erodes the distinctive local character of some of our plant communities (Dines 2016). An example of this is planting Common Poppy, Cornflower, Corn Marigold, Corncockle and Corn Chamomile together, a combination which never appears naturally in any British arable field, and where the Corn Chamomile is probably Austrian Chamomile(Dines *loc. cit.*). The unique mixtures of flowers in our meadows help us define our sense of place. He says quite rightly that the charity Plantlife "is a plant-conservation charity not a flower-appreciation society." A variation of this is the large-scale planting of garden varieties of daffodils on our roadside verges, so called "horticultural bling".[129] This has been described by Andy Tasker as "like painting lipstick on the Mona Lisa."[130] So-called "seed-packet habitats" are the equivalent of drinking a fizzy energy drink, rather than eating a balanced diet for long-term health.[131]

Man deliberately introduced new species into the UK for three main reasons – economic, ornamental and sporting (Lever 1977). Lever (*loc. cit.*) breaks down these categories further by suggesting that economic reasons can be for food or skins, e.g. the Pheasant was introduced for food and the Mink was introduced for fur; the Rabbit was introduced for both. Some species were probably introduced for a mix of reasons, e.g. the Grass Carp was originally introduced to the UK in the 1960s to control aquatic vegetation but is now also useful as a food resource and for angling.[132]

Economic reasons:
- For industrial purposes – the Oak Marble Gall Wasp was introduced to make ink (the galls contain large amounts of tannic acid, which was used for making iron gall ink and for dyeing cloth) but it needed the Turkey Oak (introduced in 1735) to complete its life cycle. It is now common everywhere, whether there are Turkey Oaks or not (Rackham 2019).

- For agriculture – there are many examples here, such as the Apple which is thought to have originated in Central Asia where its primary ancestor, *Malus sieversii*, is native to the foothills between western China and the former Soviet Union. The rise of the Roman Empire spread cultivation of the domestic apple north and west into Europe. Apple cores thrown from car windows are changing our native flora.[133] Another example is

129. People have even planted cultivated daffodils in woods where rare native Wild Daffodils occur (Twitcher in the Swamp, *British Wildlife* 2020 31(4): 309).
130. *Daily Telegraph* 17 October 2016.
131. Plantlife's *Keeping the wild in wildflower* – http://www.plantlife.org.uk/uk/our-work/campaigning-change/keeping-wild-wildflower
132. They spawn in water temperatures well in excess of 20 degrees C and therefore are unable to breed naturally in the UK.
133. *Daily Telegraph* 30 December 2019: tossing apple cores out of the car window could be destroying Britain's last wild apple trees. Trees which have sprouted from supermarket varieties have been found growing along the verges of motorways. Genetic studies of Crab Apple trees – Britain's last wild variety – show that in some areas more than half are now hybrids, after cross-pollinating with

the introduction of 282 long-tongued bumblebees (*Bombus terrestris* and *Bombus ruderatus*) via the Steamship *Tongariro* from London to Christchurch New Zealand in 1884 to act as pollinators for the Red Clover that farmers had brought over from England but which could not produce seed as there were no natural pollinators there (Juniper 2013).

- For biological control – the sap-sucking psyllid *Aphalara itadori* was introduced in England in 2010 (with releases until 2014) in a trial to see if they could help stop the spread of Japanese Knotweed by natural control. This psyllid is restricted to Japanese Knotweed in its native Japan. There were more releases from 2015–2016. The numbers of the psyllid went down over the summer and there was minimal overwintering survival. There were more releases in 2017 and 2018 including stock reared from outdoor overwintered adults in an attempt to improve winter survival – but overwintering survival observed in the Midlands, south-east and south-west England was again minimal. No releases were made in 2019. A survey to Japan was carried out in June 2019 to collect psyllids better climatically matched to UK conditions and at the time of writing research was continuing on new cultures.[134]

Ornamental reasons:
- For garden and parklands – the Turkey Oak is the fastest growing oak in Britain, tolerating poor soils and atmospheric pollution, and was widely planted in Victorian times as an ornamental tree (Rose 2017). The first acorns were sent to the Exeter nurseryman William Lucombe in 1725 labelled Turkey Oaks; it was first recorded growing wild in Britain in 1905 and is now fully naturalised. It brought with it the Knopper Gall Wasp (Rackham 2019) which makes galls in the acorns of Pedunculate Oak, making these acorns inviable, and possibly affecting the natural regeneration of Pedunculate Oak (Rose 2017).[135]

- For beauty and charm – The lovely Jersey Tiger moth[136] may have been deliberately introduced to Britain from the Channel Islands in the 19th century although it may alternatively have arrived as a passenger on

---

domesticated varieties.
134. Press release by CABI January 2020.
135. Despite concerns over its place in the natural environment, Turkey Oaks can support a range of saproxylic invertebrates (e.g. Whitehead 1996) and are preferred for hoarding by Jays and Squirrels due to the high tannin content and slower germination speed of the acorns (Rose 2017). Rose (2017) states: "The demonisation of Turkey Oak would surely lead to unnecessary removals, and naturalist will therefore need to communicate to the wide British public that the spread of the species is not purely detrimental."
136. On the Isle of Rhodes there is a Valley of the Butterflies where tourists are taken by bus to see the wonder of thousands of Jersey Tigers aestivating in a wooded valley where signs say "do not throw woods at the butterflies" (if you do you can get the Jersey Tigers to open their wings and display the bright red or yellow underwing); imagine how many tourists would pay to visit the Valley of the Moths!

"fishing smacks and luggers" or even on imported plants (Allan 1948). The Map Butterfly[137] is especially beautiful as it has two forms – an orange spring form (*levana*) and an autumn black form (*prorsa*); it was deliberately introduced into the Forest of Dean in 1912, but deliberately collected out by the entomologist A.B. Farn who was opposed to having a foreign species here. The spectacular Purple Emperor was re-introduced into Fermyn Wood in 1973 – with additional stock releases for at least 25 years – by Denys Watkins-Pitchford (although Oates (2020) considers that it may have survived here at low densities all along); it is now probably the easiest place in Britain to see Purple Emperors and at weekends each Purple Emperor attracted to the ground by oriental shrimp paste can be surrounded by up to 20 photographers, and each butterfly may be photographed hundreds of times.

Sporting reasons:

- For hunting – The Irish Hare is a subspecies of the Mountain Hare which colonised Ireland during the Ice Age, probably via a southerly landmass now submerged (Reid 2018). In the absence of Brown Hare, the Irish Hare descended from high elevations and began to occupy most of the available habitat. Then Brown Hares were introduced into Ireland in Donegal, Fermanagh, Londonderry and Tyrone between 1848 and the 1890s by enthusiasts of hare coursing (Harris & Yalden 2008); although it is relatively scarce compared to the Irish Hare it is spreading by up to 2km a year (Reid 2018) and there appears to be an active invasive-native species replacement process at work, with climate change likely to favour the Brown Hare. Another well-known introduction for sporting reasons is the Red-legged Partridge which was first introduced to mainland Britain in 1673 when King Charles 2nd dispatched his gamekeeper Favennes de Mouchant to the Chateau de Chambord in France to obtain birds to stock the royal parks of Richmond and Windsor; the bird today is widespread across southern, central and eastern England, and sometimes on quiet country lanes the driver has to wait whilst the chicks cross the road. In fact, the Red-legged Partridge is not really suitable as a sporting bird as it tends to run rather than fly – which sportsmen would say is not really sporting.

Other reasons:

- For controlling public nuisance – In Australia, the millions of cows and sheep that were brought over with settlers produced dung pats that the native indigenous dung beetles could not adapt to or cope with, so the Australian Dung Beetle Project was started to introduce non-native dung beetles that could cope with huge amounts of dung (estimated at 33 million tonnes of dung per year[138]). Between 1968 and 1984, 1.73 million dung

137. At one time I thought about a trial introduction to Cornwall as it feeds on Nettle – I didn't actually do this but Oates & Warren (1990) thought I did!
138. https://therelevanceofdungbeetles.weebly.com/australian-dung-beetle-project.html accessed 7 February 2020.

beetles of various species were released with mixed success, with some species thriving (Jones 2017); the dung beetles bury the dung which improves pasture productivity, sequesters carbon, stops the smothering effect on grassland, and controls buffalo flies and bush flies. Introductions of dung beetles are still continuing.

- For avoidance of injury – large numbers of Red-eared Terrapins were released into ponds and rivers in Britain. Bought as cute baby turtles as a spin-off from the Teenage Mutant Ninja Turtle cartoons, as they grow they become aggressive and prone to snapping with their sharp beaks. The first records for Cornwall were at two sites in 1989, and they were still at Hayle pond in 2017, 18 years later.[139]

- For avoidance of care – Siberian Chipmunks were briefly popular in France as domestic pets after the 2007 Hollywood film *Alvin and the Chipmunks*; many were released into woodlands and in 2014 over 10,000 animals were counted in the Sénart Forest near Paris; it is estimated that there are now about 12 separate colonies in France estimated at over 150,000 individuals. They carry Lyme disease. They are often caught by cats, and one was caught by a Red-tailed Hawk flown for bird control at a landfill site in Yorkshire in 1999 (Harris & Yalden 2008).

The policies for selecting potential introduction sites for the Large Blue butterfly are chosen by the Joint Committee for the Re-establishment of the Large Blue butterfly, a multi-organisational body chaired by Jeremy Thomas.[140] Sites are not selected at random. The background to policy decisions are that the Large Blue larvae feed on Wild Thyme or Majoram and then on the grubs of the red ant *Myrmica sabuleti* on warm southerly facing sites, and that provision has to be made for future changes in habitat and aspect due to climate change and the restricted ability of the butterfly to colonise new areas (perhaps up to 3.5km distant). The following mix of scientific evidence and conservation concerns are taken into consideration when selecting sites:

- Ant survey data to determine that the red ant *Myrmica sabuleti* is present in sufficient densities and distribution across the site.
- Larval foodplant surveys to determine the distribution and abundance of Wild Thyme and/or Majoram.
- The aspect of site, priority being given to sites that have variable aspects and have sheltered areas.
- The depth of soil and susceptibility to drought.
- The strategic position of the site within its landscape and the distance to other sites (actual and potential).
- The size of the site and its potential carrying capacity for Large Blues.

---

139. The *West Briton* 28 September 2017.
140. I have been privileged to have been a member of this committee since 1987.

- The ownership of site and the committed support of owner and/or site manager.
- The deliverability and sustainability of site management, in particular grazing and scrub control.
- Designations for the site and participation (potential or actual) in agri-environment schemes.
- Public access – does the site have public access and what possible problems could be caused by visitors following an introduction.
- The ability to monitor the site.

The perception of the introduction of non-native species to control pests has changed over the years. The day-flying moth *Levuana iridescens* was considered to be endemic to the Fijian Island of Viti Levu where it feeds on coconut palms; it may have existed in small native colonies in its natural habitat along the coast until populations exploded after farmers began to plant coconut trees in large monocultures inland away from the strong coastal winds (Nazari, Tarmann & Efetov 2019). After it became a pest in the 1920s the non-native parasitoid *Bessa remota* was introduced as a biological control and effectively ended the destruction of coconut palms by *L. iridescens* in Fiji. The moth was last observed in 1956 and has been officially declared extinct by IUCN since 1996. There has been some debate over whether the moth was in fact native to Fiji but it may well be that it is an old relict that has been on Fiji for a long time and is derived directly from a primitive Australian ancestor. It may still survive in Fiji in low numbers, perhaps in small inaccessible offshore islands neighbouring Viti Levu where coconut palms are not maintained for commercial use (Nazari, Tarmann & Efetov 2019). Over recent decades, the tone of discussion around the fate of this moth has shifted from the self-congratulatory – "a classical example of successful biological control" and "best documented case of extinction" – to the worried "extinction of a native insect following the introduction of an exotic control agent" – to the "possibly not extinct at all."

Introduce – accidentally
Accidental introductions may be by-products of man's constant agitated movements around the globe or as unseen passengers on deliberate introductions; as Kolbert (2104) writes:

In any 24 hour period it is estimated that 10,000 different species are being moved round the world just in ballast water in ships. A single supertanker or jet passengers can undo millions of years of geographic separation – creating the New Pangaea – re-assembling the world into one enormous supercontinent.

Many – probably most – releases are accidental. The import of plants from foreign climes often brings the unintended import of associated fauna. Three species of stick insect can be seen on Tresco on the Isles of Scilly: the Prickly Stick Insect first recorded on Tresco in 1943, the Smooth Stick Insect first recorded on Tresco in 1949 (both accidentally imported from New Zealand) and the Corsican Stick Insect, first recorded on Tresco in 2002. The Tasmanian moth *Barea asbolaea* was first discovered in south-west Cornwall by Laurie Oakes in 2004 but was not recognised as this species until several years later when he started to see larger numbers appearing in the same locality (Oakes 2011); it was probably imported in crates holding tree ferns for a nearby nursery as long ago as the 1890s, has now started to spread and has now been found as far away as the Isle of Wight (Heckford & Beavan 2020). The Long-tailed Blue butterfly, which is a rare migrant to southern Britain, was found in Fair Isle, once definitely once probably, introduced with vegetables in 2006 and 2008. The moth *Pandesma robusta*, which originates in South Africa, was found on Fair Isle in 2004, freshly dead amongst South African grapes (Riddiford & Young 2017).

The Silver-studded Blue in Cornwall is found feeding on Common Bird's Foot Trefoil on coastal sand dunes and on heathers in heathland areas. However, on one heathland site the females lay on Common Bird's Foot Trefoil (Spalding 2009). This was a puzzle to me, especially since the nearest dunes are some 5.6km away. Then I saw a large clump of Marram Grass growing on the edge of the heath, on a small pile of sand by a concrete ramp near the railway line. Sand used to be brought by lorry from a large sand dune complex 12.2km away in the 1960s and subsequently stored in a depot ready for use either as a surface dressing on the fields or as grit for the roads in winter when the salt from sea spray in the sand was an added bonus. The clump of Marram presumably arrived by lorry from the dunes as seed or rootstock in the sand. Silver-studded Blues probably arrived the same way during the winter as eggs on plant material. They are unlikely to have arrived without assistance as they rarely travel more than 4km, usually moving less than 20m per day (Asher *et al.* 2001). Silver-studded Blues appear to be reluctant to change foodplant (Thomas, C.D. *et al.* 1999), although in 2020 there were some signs that the butterflies were beginning to feed on heathers at this site.

The presence of the Sandhill Rustic moth on an isolated shingle beach in Cornwall, more than 300km from any other known sites, is hard to explain. A deliberate introduction would have been very unlikely and would have had to have taken place many years ago to give time for the moths to become cryptic in their shingle habitat, but a possible explanation is that the moths could have arrived here as the accidental result of a shipwreck, the cargo spilling onto the beach, or perhaps even on the larval foodplant Sand Couch used as packing for wine casks, which is how Irish Heath may have arrived in Ireland (Doyle 1990) – or even on a floating raft of vegetation from sites in Brittany on the other side of the English Channel. Nearby in Cornwall, after the Italian grain ship *Espagnol* was wrecked in Acton Cove near Marazion in 1875, the whole of the surrounding area was swarming with Black Rats (Lever 1977), an unwelcome introduction. With the Sandhill Rustic it can be hard to tell whether man has had a role or not. One theory is that the moth has survived in its beach habitat since the last ice age, surviving on the beach as it was pushed upwards by the rising sea water as the ice melted.

The Harlequin Ladybird originates from eastern Russia, China and Japan but was introduced to the USA (in 1916) and Europe (in the 1980s) to control aphids. However, they arrived in Britain accidentally (as far as is known) either with the assistance of the wind or in fruit and vegetables, being first recorded in Essex in 2004. Their introduction and subsequent rapid spread has had a major negative effect on native ladybirds, especially the Two-Spot Ladybird, which is smaller and weaker and which substantially overlap in the timing of their appearance (Brown & Roy 2018).

Even in Antarctica – which is the area in the world least invaded by non-native species due to its geographic isolation, harsh climate and limited history of human activity – there are non-native species. There are five non-native invertebrate species currently on terrestrial Antarctica (Bartlett *et al.* 2020), of which the most persistent is the flightless midge *Eretmoptera murphyi*. Native to sub-Antarctic Georgia, it is now established on Signy Island in South Orkney at 60°S, and spreading along routes scientists take to visit their research sites on the island. As a detritivore, it may accelerate nutrient recycling which may have wide impacts on the biodiversity of the island.

It is now possible to use DNA profiling to investigate whether the movement of an invasive species has been influenced by man. Signorile *et al.* (2016) built up a genotype database of 1421 individuals of the Grey Squirrel from 59 locations across Europe and one in the USA to allow them to compare the DNA of newly detected populations with the DNA of known individuals, so that they could identify where animals came from and identify invasion pathways. Their results indicated illegal human-mediated translocations in Aberdeen, the Isle of Skye and Northumberland in the UK, and revealed precise details of the illegal squirrel trade in Italy. We know that people often move animals around the UK; the release of butterflies is especially prevalent. DNA sequencing showed that an unexpected colony of Marsh Fritillary in the UK Midlands was genetically distant from surrounding colonies (Joyce & Pullin 2003) which created a puzzle until Domino Joyce was told that someone had been releasing butterflies from France.

Eradicate
Man often tries to manage nature by eradication. The classic case is perhaps the attempt in China by Mao Zedong in his war on pests, launched as part of his Great Leap Forward, an attempt to change in just five years the predominantly farming society to a modern, industrial society (Juniper 2013). He issued a directive to do away with all pests, especially sparrows, rats, mosquitoes and flies. Nature was demonised as man's adversary, a force to be resisted, subjugated and overcome. In Shanghai alone the death of 1,367,440 sparrows was recorded. But – released from sparrows – locusts and other pests devoured the crops, and this, coupled with attempts by bureaucrats to hide the failure of crops by taking most of the harvest into the cities, resulted in huge numbers of people starving to death.

This is an extreme example and shows the problems of interfering without understanding. Closer to home, and very successfully, I was involved in the Isles of Scilly Seabird Recovery Project which aimed to reverse declines in seabird populations on St Agnes and Gugh by the removal of the Brown Rat[141]. These rats predated the birds, in particular ground-nesting Storm Petrel and Manx Shearwater where they nested in colonies in burrows amongst cushions of Thrift growing in the soft coastal sand; here they were terribly vulnerable to rats. The aim was to eliminate rats entirely from these islands, protected as they were from St Mary's (the largest island in the Scillies) and the other islands by deep water with tidal currents too strong for rats to swim across the channel. The operation was a great success, these two islands being declared rat free on 13th February 2016, with the first Manx Shearwater chick in living memory being recorded in September 2014 on St Agnes and Gugh and the first recorded Storm Petrol chicks to have survived on St Agnes and Gugh in living memory recorded in September 2015.[142]

We[143] carried out the programme to monitor the changing wildlife of these two islands, surveying birds, rabbits, plants, invertebrates and the Scilly Shrew (or Lesser White-Toothed Shrew). The island of Bryher was chosen as the control site (there was no rat removal programme here), so that changes on St Agnes and Gugh could be compared with changes on Bryher, with any differences possibly due at least partly to the removal of rats. A huge amount of data was collected and collated for 2013 and 2014; for example, 8195 invertebrates were collected in pitfall traps on St Agnes alone in 2013, increasing to 19,959 in 2014. We found a number of new beetles for St Agnes and Gugh and a new species for the Isles of Scilly. As a by-product of rat removal, numbers of Scilly Shrew increased dramatically on both Gugh and St Agnes;[144] further proof of rat predation was shown by the dissection of the stomach contents of 50 rats, where 18% were found to contain the remains of Scilly Shrews. Shrews began turning up in people's houses, brought in by cats, probably their other main predator. Numbers declined on Bryher, so that we can be pretty sure that increases on St Agnes and Gugh were due directly to the rat removal. Scilly Shrews feed regularly on Landhoppers and numbers recorded went down on St Agnes, perhaps in part to the increased abundance of Shrews.[145]

---

141. The Brown Rat itself is an accidental introduction, probably reaching England around 1720 in shipping from Russia (Harris & Yalden 2008).
142. https://www.ios-seabirds.org.uk/ accessed 6 March 2020.
143. Spalding Associates (Environmental) Ltd.
144. On Gugh the total number of tunnels with Scilly Shrew prints in them increased from 12 out of 120 tunnels in 2013 to 111 out of 120 tunnels in 2016; on St Agnes the total number of tunnels with shrew prints in them increased from 3/120 tunnels in 2013 to 25/120 tunnels in 2016 (with a peak of 31/120 tunnels in 2015); on Bryher the total number of tunnels with shrew prints in them reduced from 34/120 tunnels in 2013 to 12/120 tunnels in 2015 and 2016 (with a drop to 3/120 tunnels in 2014).
145. The Landhopper is itself a non-native, being a subtropical species native to the forests of New South Wales (Gregory 2016) and its distribution in Britain and Ireland exhibits a close correlation with mean January 5°C isotherm (Harding & Sutton 1988).

Eradication in the UK nowadays is possibly mainly of alien species. I have been involved for many years in eradication programmes for Japanese Knotweed as part of the planning process. It is an offence under Schedule 9 of the Wildlife and Countryside Act 1981 (as amended) to plant or otherwise encourage the growth of Japanese Knotweed in the wild. It is therefore illegal to spread Japanese Knotweed, and cutting the plant or roots and/or disturbing the surrounding soil may encourage its spread if not correctly managed. An amendment to the Anti-social Behaviour, Crime and Policing Act (2014) states that landowners could be reasonably expected to control Japanese Knotweed if it is present on their land, and if its presence is "having a detrimental effect on the quality of life of those in the local community" then "failure to act" can be deemed as anti-social conduct. As a result, mortgage companies are often reluctant to grant mortgages on properties where Japanese Knotweed occurs. It may be difficult to eradicate entirely; treatment by glyphosate will reduce vigour but too much regular treatment may result in so-called "bonsai" knotweed, where the knotweed survives but in a resistant dwarf form. Various other effective treatments are available.

The top ten invasive threats to Europe according to the *New Scientist* (2016. No 3063) are:

Alligator Weed *Alternanthera philoxeroides*
Devil Firefish *Pterois miles*
Small Asian Mongoose *Herpestes javanicus*
Finlayson's Squirrel *Callosciurus finlaysonii*
Common Kingsnake *Lampropeltis getula*
Golden Mussel *Limnoperna fortunei*
Rusty Crayfish *Faxonius rusticus*
Northern Brown Shrimp *Farfantepenaeus aztecus*
Western Mosquitofish *Gambusia affinis*
Striped Eel Catfish *Plotosus lineatus*

Monitor

Scientists spend a considerable amount of time monitoring wild species. Sometimes they can be monitored to extinction. There is a difference between the scientist, interested in seeing what goes on and how a species responds to changing conditions, and the conservationist, wanting to respond to monitored changes by taking action to halt declines. Sometimes the scientist and the conservationist are the same person. The UK Butterfly Monitoring Scheme collects annual data on the population status of butterflies; a significant part of this data comes from regular transects along fixed routes (so-called Pollard Walks after Ernie Pollard who helped design these walks). Data from these transects can be used to provide indications as to the changing state of the environment, in particular the impacts of climate change.

I adapted the butterfly transect methodology for use at night with the Sandhill Rustic moth (Spalding 1997) and the methodology was further refined for use with most nocturnal moths by Birkenshaw & Thomas (1999). For the Sandhill Rustic I have monitored the population every year from 1995 to 2020 – and continuing. The Index of Abundance (the sum of the weekly means over a flight period varying between 3 and 7 weeks)[146] ranged from as low as 6.5 to as high as 58, but there was a heart-stopping moment in 2014 when I saw none at all in August and the Index went down to 3, based on a total of just 3 individuals (all female) seen over 3 weeks between 1st and 19th September, and I thought perhaps I had been monitoring it to extinction. The following year the Index went up to 28.5. The moth occurs on a shingle beach and there are no easy management solutions. Is there any point in monitoring where there is little possibility of action? The caterpillars feed on Sand Couch Grass and it is possible to clear areas of the shingle beach to increase habitat suitability for this grass, with the hope that the moth will take advantage of this. A translocation of grass[147] when work was being carried out on the beach was successful, as a single moth was seen the following autumn sitting on a translocated clump of grass. Scientifically, it would have been fascinating if the moth had become extinct here; conservationally, it would have been a disaster. It is interesting that it survived – there must have been at least one male present in 2014 and it is of real interest that the population can recover from such low numbers. Why did it decline so drastically? One possible reason is the action of the sea, with waves washing over the habitat during the winter storms and leaving heavy traces of salt washed down into the sand, into which the larva move in early spring to feed on the grass rhizomes.

Manage

Nature reserves are usually managed (at least partly) for wildlife. Management may not be easy and sometimes there are unpredictable consequences. The Chipman Valley (also known as Butterfly Valley) in north Cornwall was fenced off in the 1930s to conserve the Large Blue butterfly but the vegetation – previously kept short by grazing – grew longer and the Large Blue disappeared.

Sometimes there are competing interests for management, e.g. management for short turf early successional stage species such as Large Blue butterflies may compete with longer turf species such as Duke of Burgundy, and these competing interests may be served by separating reserves into compartments. Decisions are made according to the perceived value of the different species that will benefit from management recommendations; preferences between different butterfly species may be easy to determine, but deciding between management for rare plants or rare birds may be more difficult and may involve satisfying different stakeholders (individuals and organised charities) with different objectives. At one point during consideration of management of north Atlantic coastal sites in Devon

146. Generally, 4–5 weeks for the Sandhill Rustic; the moths usually start to emerge around 15th August and go on until the end of September, with two records for 1 October (2013 and 2015).
147. Very simply by carefully lifting clumps of Sand Couch Grass inside an excavator bucket so that the clumps remained undisturbed and placing them carefully into the new receptor area.

and Cornwall for Large Blue butterflies, one of the key stakeholders representing the Rural Development Service refused to support the proposal since it was a single species initiative, but then praised the Cirl Bunting Project in Devon as an example to follow, without appearing to understand that the Cirl Bunting Project was single species initiative, with the following objectives[148]:

- To reach 1000 pairs of Cirl Buntings by 2020 or sooner and a population which is stable or increasing.
- To offer advice and support to landowners within the bird's current range and to promote sympathetic land management for the Cirl Bunting.
- To develop a network of sympathetically-managed sites throughout the Cirl Bunting's current range.
- To work with Natural England, local authorities and developers to ensure that the impacts of development are minimised and offset.
- To establish a self-sustaining geographically separate population.

In fact, the Large Blue project can show that a range of other species benefit from targeted management for short turf grassland with abundant Wild Thyme. For example, at the Large Blue introduction site at Dannonchapel in north Cornwall, the following species were recorded for the first time or increased in abundance: Pale Flowered Violet, Adder, Green Tiger Beetle, Kugelann's Ground Beetle, Silver-studded Blue and the solitary mining bee *Panurgus banksianus*. Kugelann's Ground Beetle was previously only known in Cornwall from West Penwith in 1936; whilst having lunch with Dave Bilton and Pete Smithers from Plymouth University – I saw it and Dave identified it.

The Heath Lobelia is a rare plant confined in southern Britain to 6–7 sites. It is found on infertile acidic soils, often seasonally waterlogged, and populations fluctuate erratically in size. Some attempts have been made to translocate plants. In Cornwall it is only found at Redlake Cottage Meadows nature reserve, managed by Cornwall Wildlife Trust. The plant has a bitter after taste in the mouth. I used to count the number of flowerheads as part of a monitoring programme but since it is a rhizomatous plant it is impossible to be certain of the number of separate plants. Management was by careful scrub clearance. The number of plants was down to single figures in the early 1980s and then a Manpower Services Team was employed to clear the scrub; against advice, they built a huge fire to burn the cut material and played football on the site whilst waiting for the fire to burn down. Next year, there were scores of Heath Lobelia across the site. Now we know that germination seems to be stimulated by disturbance (Preston, Pearman & Dines 2002). Wildlife will often do its own thing, regardless of, and despite, man's efforts to control it.

---

148. https://www.rspb.org.uk/our-work/conservation/projects/cirl-bunting-project/ accessed 9 March 2020.

Rewilding

A new recent initiative is the aim to rewild the countryside. There are two competing views – back out and let nature take its course in a man-free environment or a controlled re-wilding where man decides on the target habitats and species. The former as a deliberate policy would only be possible on a remote island in the middle of the ocean, and Man's influence would reach even there if only as a result of man-induced climate change. In a controlled re-wilding, the role man plays may be to kick-start the action and settle back and see where it goes, or steer nature in the desired direction. Rewilding differs from species release and introduction – which are intimately controlled by man – as it takes a holistic view at a landscape scale where man takes a back seat and lets nature play the major role. The devil is in the detail. At the moment human dominance over nature has become so complete that we have altered almost everything and whether we intervene or not the outcomes are culturally determined; we can't ignore the "figure in the landscape" (Rotherham 2014). A schism has opened up between those who want feral nature to run free and those who want to interfere and manage.

For example, the charity Rewilding Britain[149] aims to make rewilding a reality for people and nature. They talk about encouraging a balance between people and the rest of nature where each can thrive and for people to re-connect with wild nature. For them, rewilding brings nature back to life in a way that excites people; it is not about excluding people. It draws people in to connect with nature – to find peace or adventure, to relax or re-energise, to explore or rest. Rewilding areas provide opportunities for outdoor activities such as walking, viewing wildlife, hunting, fishing, and more. It helps people experience the wonder and enchantment of wild nature. It can help improve health and wellbeing and deliver a range of social benefits for young people.

They have four key principles of rewilding:
- People, communities and livelihoods are key.

- Natural processes drive outcomes – rewilding goes where nature takes it. Rewilding seeks to reinstate natural processes. Management is only necessary in core areas where natural processes are missing. The reintroduction of missing species may be a necessary part of rewilding where it's needed to achieve the full range of natural processes and healthy functioning ecosystems.

- Work at nature's scale – rewilding needs sufficient scale so that nature can reinstate natural processes and create ecologically coherent units.

- Benefits are for the long term – Rewilding is an opportunity to leave a positive legacy for future generations.

---

149. http://www.rewildingbritain.org.uk/

For many people, this would not be about re-wilding but rather adapting a larger, landscape scale nature for people, for their healthy lifestyle and social care, creating a more natural park in which people can visit and walk in a natural space. In this context, rewilding is a framework for reducing management and restoring natural processes but not for taking farming completely out of the landscape.

This is perhaps a reversion to a recent past when man was less dominant but still very much in control. This brings us to one of the key questions about rewilding – if it aims as reversion to the past, how far back do we go? We will probably never know what was the natural landscape of pre-human Europe – was it a closed canopy forest where carnivores roamed controlling herbivore populations or an open park-like landscape where large herbivores grazed in peace (King 2017)? If we look at bird life, only 25% of British bird species are woodland specialists, whereas 75% are species of grassland, scrub or mixed habitats; this may suggest that the pre-human landscape was probably more open and grazed than is generally believed (King 2017).

Monbiot (2014) suggests that the conservation movement "has sought to freeze living systems in time … conservation often looks to the past … (whereas) rewilding … looks to the future." He is more ambitious than most. For him, rewilding is not an attempt to restore natural ecosystems to any prior state but to permit ecological processes to resume. Rewilding has no end points, no view about what a "right" ecosystem or a "right" assemblage of species looks like – "it lets nature decide." He explains correctly that many of the places ecologists have studied have already been radically altered by human intervention and many of the processes they have recorded which they assumed were natural appear to have been shaped as much by people and their domestic stock as by wild animals and plants, thus giving a false impression of how wildlife behaves in a natural environment. Roosevelt (1909–1910) writes how large animals – Lion, Elephant, Leopard, Buffalo – in Africa became nocturnal when the European colonists appeared with their guns; only the Rhinoceros refused to change its behaviour. In the northern highlands of Scotland, in Sutherland, the Badger appears early each day in summer, when still daylight, perhaps partly as a result of the shorter nights but also as a result of the lower incidence of disturbance; in heavily populated areas Badgers wait for dark before it is safe to emerge. In contrast, in Berlin, Wild Boars have become so accustomed to city life that they cross the roads at traffic lights.[150]

Monbiot (2014) has prepared a list of large animals and birds to be considered for re-introduction; he has scored each (1–10) with high scores for suitable species likely to succeed, be politically acceptable and likely to help restore dynamic ecological processes. I have listed them in order of suitability (Table 4.1). Some of these species are already in the UK, such as Wild Boar, Osprey, White Stork, Great Bustard, Spoonbill, Night Heron and Reindeer. Bison were released in an enclosure

---

150. There are 2–3000 Wild Boar in Berlin, many of which cross at traffic lights (*The Times* 14 March 2020).

at the Alladale Wilderness Reserve in 2011, but the project was terminated in 2013 partly due to a TB outbreak in the UK (meaning that a bull was never introduced into the herd) and partly because the cows never settled properly and proved very dangerous for their handlers[151]. The White-tailed Sea Eagle is a magnificent bird; I saw one close at hand when staying at Lower Diabaig – it was a young bird resting on a gate post; when it flew off its wings seemed to take up the whole width of the track. Beavers are back; in the early days one considered location by Derek Gow was the White River catchment from St Austell in Mevagissey where the Beavers would have been contained by the urban environment of St Austell in the north and the sea in the south. This project never got off the ground but Derek has successfully introduced them into other places.[152] The Common Crane is back in the Somerset Levels as part of the RSPB's Great Crane Project; Jenny Pearson, who worked with me in Truro, undertook a university research project on these birds and showed us around – you can sometimes see the Cranes as you drive past on the M5, tall unmistakable light grey birds.[153]

Other proposed animal reintroductions are perhaps more controversial such as Lynx, Wolf and Wolverine. Wolves became extinct in the UK with the last definite record being an animal killed in Sutherland in 1621, although there is a record of wolf in the Findhorn Valley in 1743. Monbiot (2014) states: "I want to see wolves reintroduced because wolves are fascinating …. they feel to me like the shadow that fleets between the systole and the diastole, because they are the necessary monsters of the mind, inhabitants of the more passionate world against which we have locked our doors." In France the wolf disappeared as late as 1937 and returned in 1992; there are currently more than 500 wolves in France (mainly in the south-east)[154] and about 80 packs, with a few erratic wondering wolves found beyond the known areas. Each year in France, several thousand domestic animals, mainly sheep, are victims of the predation attributed to the wolf and several measures have been suggested to reduce the number of attacks.[155] To make the presence of the wolf acceptable, it is necessary to profoundly change agricultural and hunting practices in a number of areas and to consider that a large part of the country is a vast garden where wildlife and open spaces are not enough for wolves to live there without over-reliance on domestic species.[156] So to keep the wolves

151. There is a free-ranging population of European Bison in the huge Białowieża Forest of Belarus and Poland where we went for a meeting of the Societas Europaea Lepidopterologica. European Bison became extinct in the wild after the 1st World War but some were released here in 1952. They have now been re-introduced to other countries e.g. Romania in the Carpathian Mountains from 2004.
152. I know them from Brittany where five families were introduced in the Monts d'Arrée region surrounding the Réservoir Saint-Michel. The farmers were against them and some were shot, but we managed to see them during a field trip I was leading for the Field Studies Council, swimming at dusk, above their low dam, dark heads just above the sky-reflected water. Even in Scotland, after becoming full European Protected Species since 1 May 2019, some 87 have been shot in an attempt to manage them and their dams (*Daily Telegraph* 28 May 2020).
153. By train you might be able to see the Cranes at Langport and the Large Blues two minutes later on the same line to Paddington.
154. http://www.loupfrance.fr/suivi-du-loup/situation-du-loup-en-france/ accessed 26 March 2020.
155. https://www.ferus.fr/loup/le-loup-et-les-troupeaux accessed 26 March 2020.
156. Francois de Beaulieu personal commentary; he is the author of *Quand on parle du loup en Bre-*

here means that farming techniques have to change and the wolf itself depends largely on domestic animals for its survival.

There is no chance that Bear, Elephant, Hippopotamus, Lion and Spotted Hyena will ever be re-introduced into the wild[157]; the ultimate rewilding – for dangerous animals to be introduced and allowed to predate humans – will never be allowed.

Table 4.1. Potential species for re-introduction, scored for suitability (10 = suitable; 1 = not suitable) from Monbiot 2014.

Name	Score
Beaver	10
Wild Boar	10
Elk or Moose	10
Blue Stag Beetle	10
White-tailed Sea Eagle	10
Osprey	10
Goshawk	10
Capercaillie	10
Common Crane	10
White Stork	10
Spoonbill	10
Night Heron	10
Dalmatian Pelican	10
Great Bustard	9
Lynx	9
European Sturgeon	8
Eagle Owl	7
Bison	7
Wolf	7
Grey Whale	7
Wolverine	4
Hazel Grouse	3
Wild Horse	3
Bear	3
Reindeer	2
Elephant	2
Black Rhinoceros	2
Walrus	2
Lion	1
Spotted Hyena	1
Hippopotamus	1

An example of rewilding on a large scale is the Pleistocene Park established in north-eastern Siberia in the Sakha (Yakutia) republic[158] by Sergey Zimov and others in 1988; the park closed then restarted in 1996 with 144km² of land of which 20km² is enclosed. Zimov and colleagues hypothesised that the current wet, shrub and moss-dominated tundra is largely a consequence of the demise of

---

tagne Éditions Le Télégramme 2005.
157. Until around 40,000 years ago, the Straight-Tusked Elephant roamed across much of Europe. Three species of rhino and hippos wandered around southern Britain and Lions hunted Reindeer.
158. The weather there at the time of writing (04.00 hours on 25 March 2020) was -18ºC, dropping to -25ºC at midnight.

the Ice Age giants, the Woolly Mammoth, Woolly Rhinoceros, Horse, Bison and Musk Ox. It is a major initiative to restore the mammoth steppe ecosystem, which was dominant in the Arctic in the late Pleistocene, when large herbivores feeding on grasses controlled invasive mosses, evergreen shrubs and larch trees until Man killed the large herbivores. In the perception of most modern people the Arctic is an intact piece of wild nature, but the original wild ecosystems here were destroyed by humans over ten thousand years ago and current animal density in the Arctic is estimated at least one hundred times lower than during the Pleistocene.[159] With the reduction of animal numbers hay and litter accumulated on the pastures, nutrient turnover slowed down and a few centuries later low-productive vegetation took over. The rewilding project involves the replacement of the current unproductive northern ecosystems by highly productive pastures which have a high animal density. Grasses have become the dominant vegetation at many locations and there are plans to introduce predators to the ecosystem. The first animals introduced were Yakutian horses, moose and reindeer, followed by Musk Ox from the Wrangel Island, European Bison from near Moscow, Yaks, Kalmykain cows and sheep from the Lake Baikal region. However, the main purpose now is to help preserve the permafrost[160] – animal-affected soils are more than 2°C cooler and capture and store more carbon now that the large herbivores have mediated a major shift in vegetation – rather than the wild animals that occupy these areas.

What would John Muir – the Scottish-American advocate for the preservation of wilderness in the United States of America – have thought about present day nature conservation; he advocated preservation of the forests, rivers and mountains not for Man but from Man, for themselves (Wulf 2015).

---

159. https://pleistocenepark.ru/science/ accessed 25 March 2020.
160. *Newsweek* 28 January 2020.

CHAPTER 5. MIGRANT SPECIES

In this chapter I discuss just those self-propelled species and those carried by natural forces (such as the wind and the tide), not species directly moved either deliberately or accidentally by man. These migrants can be of high value in people's lives, from dragonflies, butterflies, moths and birds. This is one of the main ways nowadays that people interact with wildlife, rather than with the abstract concept of "Nature." The arrival in Britain of a rare species, travelling on its own unaided by Man, is an expression of wildness, naturalness and unexpectedness in an otherwise seemingly ordered and controlled world. It becomes a memorable occasion, a story to tell. On 13th October 1985 I travelled with my friend Steve Madge to Rame Church in the Rame peninsula just west of Plymouth where a male Wilson's Warbler had been spotted just before dusk the previous evening. We were there at dawn and Steve scoped the bushes and hedges without success with his telescope. The bird was never seen again and it was thought that it might have been eaten by the local cat. Then exactly 30 years later, to the day, another male Wilson's Warbler turned up on the Isle of Lewis. It should have travelled southwards *en route* to its wintering area in Central and South America, but in both cases they were probably caught up in Atlantic storms with westerly gales blowing them off course. There was huge excitement in 2015 in birding circles, with people travelling up to Stornaway to see this rare bird at a cost of over £450 each on a return chartered light aircraft from the Midlands to Stornoway for a day visit: "they arrived bleary-eyed and dishevelled after a sleepless night, and immediately they turned up they were in action searching for the bird."[161] For almost everyone – or perhaps everyone, unless they'd seen the bird in America – this would be a lifer, the very first time they had seen the bird, and a hugely memorable experience. "You always remember your first."[162] I can even remember **not** seeing the Wilson's Warbler.

The British Ornithologists' Union[163] (BOU) maintains the British List, the official list of wild bird records in Great Britain (England, Scotland and Wales and associated waters), managed by their Records Committee. Each species on the List is assigned to a species category; only those species in Categories A, B and C form the British List. Species in Category A are those which have been recorded in an apparently natural state at least once since 1 January 1950. Wilson's Warbler is listed here as a vagrant. Species in Category B have been recorded in an apparently natural state at least once between 1 January 1800 and 31 December 1949, but have not been recorded since. Species in Category C, although introduced, now derive from the resulting self-sustaining populations.[164] Category E comprises those species that have been recorded as introductions, human-assisted transportees or

---

161. *Daily Express* 16 October 2015.
162. https://birdsearcher.com/blog/what-is-a-lifer-in-birding/ accessed 30 March 2020.
163. https://www.bou.org.uk/
164. Category D species are those that would otherwise appear in Category A except that there is reasonable doubt that they have ever occurred in a natural state. Category F species are those recorded before 1800.

escapees from captivity, whose breeding populations (if any) are thought not to be self-sustaining – these species are not considered in the present chapter. In 1986 the BOU amended the definitions regarding ship-assisted vagrants that were barred from Category A from birds "which have certainly arrived with ship assistance" to birds which "certainly arrived with a combination of ship and human assistance, including the provision of food and shelter." A Grey Catbird was discovered on the liner QE2 on 21st October 1998 when the ship docked at Southampton, having sailed from New York, but this record could not be accepted as it was deemed the bird had been 'ship assisted' – it would have been the first British record.

There are four different but overlapping concepts of migration (Dingle & Drake 2007):

- Concept 1: A type of locomotory activity which is persistent, undistracted and straightened out.
- Concept 2: The relocation of the animal at a greater scale than normal.
- Concept 3: The seasonal to and fro movement of populations.
- Concept 4: Movements leading to a redistribution of individuals within a spatially extended population.

These definitions concern individuals that are self-propelled and/or carried by natural forces – by wind or tide – although there may be active movement into and out of the wind or current. In this chapter we are concerned mainly with concepts 1, 2 and 3. These migrants are not carried directly by man, and not affected by man except in so far as we are contributing to climate change (resulting for example in stronger winds) and changing habitats. This migratory behaviour is "persistent and straightened-out movement affected by the animal's own locomotory exertions or by its active embarkation on a vehicle" (Kennedy 1985) – by vehicle he includes winds and sea currents that the migrant species actively embarks on – but is then carried by the wind or tide. Flying insects, in order to obtain wind-assisted migration, need to fly outside their 'flight boundary layer' (the layer of the atmosphere within which the insects' self-powered flight speed exceeds the wind speed). It is especially interesting to Man when these migrants veer off course or are carried beyond their normal range or in greater than normal numbers.

Many migrations are one-way, with no population route cyclicity. This is known for many insects, e.g. wide-ranging moth pests of crops such as the European Corn Borer. In laboratory experiments adult moths were each tethered to round-about flight mills in an environmental chamber, with the data being relayed to a computer (Dorhout, Sappington & Rice 2008). There appears to be an obligatory migratory flight by unmated females in the first night after emerging from their pupae; mated moths could not be tested before the second day after emergence because the first night was needed for mating. The females fly twice as fast as the males, sometimes flying all night; flight duration declined after the first night. Flights by males and older females represented foraging flight rather than migratory flight. This explains why the European Corn Borer is a relatively common visitor to the UK shores (there were 48 records in Devon in 2019[165]) and is now resident in parts of southern England and East Anglia (Sterling & Parsons 2012); most records do not specify the sex of the individual, which is a shame as this would provide interesting additional information. The males are generally smaller and darker with pale brown or greyish brown forewings, whereas the females are generally pale yellow to light brown in color.

These migrations are also influenced by stochastic forces, which may alter the predicted pathways of known migrant species, e.g. perhaps leading to the relocation of the animal at a greater scale than normal (concept two above). When we consider what belongs in a place we have to take into account the natural movement of species both as part of their inherent ecology and as an accidental movement influenced by changing winds and currents. For those species which have a propensity to migrate (e.g. to get up into the wind) where they go is at least partly defined by the wind or sea current and not a particular pre-determined destination. Ground and air-borne radar have provided insights into how the behaviour of wind-borne migrants influences the distance travelled and the degree of dispersal during migration; these random wind effects sometimes allow these insects to find suitable habitats in unpredictable locations (Gatehouse 1997). The establishment of the European Network for the Radar surveillance of Animal Movement (ENRAM) (Shamoun-Baranes *et al.* 2019) has allowed us to track cross-European movements by birds, bats and insects.[166] Recent advances, particularly the use of vertical-looking radar, have revolutionised our knowledge of moth migration (Chapman *et al.* 2010). Moths are not simply blown along passively by the wind, but have sophisticated ways of getting to their desired destination. Silver Ys and other moths make use of high-altitude winds to achieve fast speeds (up to 55mph) and appropriate directions for their migratory movements (Chapman, Drake & Reynolds 2011). Surprisingly, by selecting the most favourable airstreams, several hundred metres above the ground, and by orientating their bodies to compensate for crosswind drift, moths are able to migrate with similar speed and efficiency to songbirds (Alerstam *et al.* 2011). Orientation typically occurs close to the downwind direction (thus ensuring that a large component of the insects' self-powered speed is directed downstream and they do not have to fight to fly upstream). In both nocturnal and more especially diurnal insects the downwind headings seem to be maintained by direct detection of wind-related turbulent cues (Hu *et al.* 2016); in this study, headings were systematically offset to the right of the flow at night-time. Orientation "performance" significantly increased with increasing flight altitude throughout the day and night, so the higher the insect flies the greater the orientation to the wind direction.

---

165. *Devon Moth Group Annual Report 2019.*
166. As well as early warning systems used to improve aviation safety by warning of large-scale bird movements.

Moths react differently depending on the wind speed. There is a compromise between moving rapidly and moving in a preferred direction of movement (Reynolds *et al.* 2016). For Silver Y the strategy has the following characteristics:

- If the wind on the night in question is highly unfavourable for movement in the preferred direction the migration is suppressed, or limited to short flights only.
- If winds are broadly favourable, but the downstream direction is more than approximately 20° from the preferred direction, the moths deviate their heading so that it lies between downstream and the preferred direction, but they do not attempt full compensation for drift.
- If winds are highly favourable, and the downstream direction is less than 20° from the preferred direction, the migrants do not make significant corrections for drift and they essentially orient downwind.

For some regular migrant species there is an overlap between concept 1 above and concept 3 (the seasonal to-and-fro movement of populations), e.g. with large southward autumn migrations in nocturnal noctuid moths such as Dark Sword-grass, Scarce Bordered Straw, Small Mottled Willow and Large Yellow Underwing (Chapman, Lim & Reynolds 2013). This is true of the Silver Y moth which is generally regarded as being incapable of overwintering in the UK although there are occasional records of larvae being found in winter (Waring & Townsend 2003). It has winter breeding regions around the Mediterranean and summer breeding regions in northern Europe. Widespread spring populations in the UK are a consequence of annual invasions from further south, so that there are often large numbers in May, June and July visiting flowers by day and moth traps by night. These moths lay eggs, produce larvae feeding on a wide range of low plants and then produce the next generation of adults which emerge in August and September; they then undertake a return migration to southern Europe and north Africa. At this time, flight activity is most intense at significantly lower altitudes than occur in spring or autumn, well below the fastest high-altitude winds, with moths flying on tailwinds from all directions (Chapman, Lim & Reynolds 2013). As a result, the Silver Y moths fly at low levels and are easily seen by lepidopterists; in Cornwall sightings peak in July and August according to the ERICA database.[167] The origins of different Silver Y generations were examined by Torniainen & Mikonranta (2018), who showed that there were clear differences in origin for different generations and that the spring generation probably emerged in central Europe; analysis of hindwings from specimens captured as long ago as 1898 showed that a warming climate may have encouraged migratory stages northwards during the last century.

---

167. ERICA = Environmental Records in Cornwall Automated, Table 5.1.

Table 5.1. All records in Cornwall for Silver Y (ERICA)

Month	1	2	3	4	5	6	7	8	9	10	11	12	Total
Sightings	10	10	11	116	493	991	2229	2371	1979	1338	285	45	9878

Red Admiral butterflies act in a similar way to Silver Ys. They fly north in the spring; there are three waves of migration seen in the UK – firstly from north Africa and southern Europe, secondly from Spain and Portugal, thirdly from central Europe (arriving in August) (Eeles 2019). Their offspring return the flight in the autumn to reach areas with conditions suitable for surviving the winter. Wind direction, low wind speed and clear skies are the most important weather variables affecting their migration (Brattström *et al.* 2008); the probability of migration is highest when a north-easterly wind of low speed occurs on sunny days with clear skies, showing that passage is largely wind-aided. This is clearest over the sea where the wind direction is more likely to be constant; on land butterflies can avoid wind effects by flying close to the ground or on the lee side of topographical features. Red Admirals sometimes fly at night; I have caught Red Admirals in my moth trap, especially when set up on the coast; when released in the autumn they can be seen to fly south (Eeles 2019). On warm days with winds from the south, Red Admiral individuals are likely to remain in their habitats. Other species observed to migrate south in the same way, but in much lower numbers, include the well-known pest species Large White (Mikkola 2003).

The Painted Lady arrives in the UK in some years in huge numbers, and observers talk about "Painted Lady Years." They too have a reverse migration in the autumn, as shown by using isotopes from wing chitin[168] (Stefanescu *et al.* 2016). Isotopes of carbon and hydrogen have also been used to determine the origins of Monarch butterflies (Miller *et al.* 2011). In north America the White-speck (or True Armyworm) is a seasonal migrant and isotope examination clearly separates the spring immigrants from the later locally produced moths in southern Ontario, Canada (Hobson *et al.* 2018).

Although the Earth's magnetic field is very weak, sufficient to deflect a compass needle but only about 100th the force of a typical fridge magnet (Al-Khalili & McFadden 2014), some birds such as Robins can detect the earth's magnetic field, distinguishing between the poles and the Equator. The activation of their magnetic compass also requires a small amount of light (around the blue end of

---

168. It is possible to use isotopes from wing chitin to link butterfly wing values to spatial hydrological hydrogen isotopic distribution (isoscapes) in precipitation. Stable isotopes are a good alternative to tagging technology as natural tracers of migration or dispersal. The principal biologically important elements (carbon, hydrogen, etc.) have each at least two stable (i.e. non-radioactive) isotopes. The ratio of each pair of stable isotopes changes over geographical gradients and these can be used to construct an isoscape map of insects with contours of equal isotope composition. This map can be used as a basemap to distinguish migrants from residents in the UK; a project was started for this using Brimstone moths collected from widely-scattered areas of the UK. Isotopes can also be used to distinguish illegally-caught insects from those purportedly purchased legally; e.g. separating English Large Blue butterflies from those caught abroad.

the spectrum) so that eyes form an important part of the process. For some time it has been clear that moths also use a compass mechanism for orientation, to guide their flight northwards in the spring and southwards in the autumn. For the Silver Y, a lunar compass was ruled out (Chapman *et al.* 2008) because the moon was below the horizon during mass-migration events or clouds obscured the moon and stars. Researchers also ruled out a stellar compass when flight took place by day as being highly unlikely (due to the poor resolution of moth compound eyes). They concluded that a geomagnetic compass was the most likely mechanism, perhaps calibrated at sunset by a solar compass similar to that of nocturnal migratory songbirds.

Monarch butterflies use a variety of senses involving sight and smell including a sun compass that can correct for the moving position of the sun during the day via its circadian clock (Reppert, Gegear & Merlin 2010). The sun compass works by comparing the height of the sun with the time of day – a relationship which varies with both longitude and latitude. This requires cryptochrome (present in the butterfly antennae[169]) to establish their circadian clock. Monarchs might also use a magnetic compass because they possess two cryptochromes that have the molecular capability for light-dependent magnetoreception. Flight simulator studies have shown that Monarchs possess an inclination magnetic compass to help direct their flight southwards in the autumn, and this compass is light-dependent, utilising ultraviolet/blue light (Guerra, Gegear & Reppert 2014). Cryptochrome-associated magnetoreception has now been discovered in a range of creatures (Dodson, Hore & Wallace 2013; Al-Khalili & McFadden 2014) and light cryptochromes have been found in the eyes of all kinds of migratory animals[170] and probably provide a magnetic field 'filter' over the bird's field of view.[171]

Where there is seasonal movement of populations, it has been suggested that there are three distinct phases of migration as the migrant species set off and then approach their destination (Mouritsen, Heyers & Güntürkün 2016). Firstly, there is a long-distance orientation phase in which the migrants use global compass cues such as celestial and geomagnetic cues to set off in particular directions and carry on over large distances. Then there is a narrowing-in phase in which the migrants use a range of local sensory cues as they near their destination, such as landmarks and sensory gradients. Then there is a pinpointing phase in which they use destination-specific sensory cues such as specific landmarks to locate their final goal.

A good example of this is shown by the Australian Bogong Moth. I have visited Australia twice and always wanted to see this fascinating moth, but so far without

169. Cryptochromes are a type of protein, found in plants and animals, that react quickly to changes in blue light. When the Monarch's antennae were painted black, the butterflies lost their circadian sense.
170. *New Scientist* 25 March 2017.
171. https://www.sciencealert.com/birds-see-magnetic-fields-cryptochrome-cry4-photoreceptor-2018 accessed 15 April 20. There is a link here to quantum physics – see for example Fay *et al.* (2019).

luck. They look unremarkable, typical brown middle-sized noctuid moths, but they make a lengthy return migration flying southwards for days or even weeks over 1000km in spring from their low-lying breeding grounds to cool high alpine caves where they aestivate in summer (Warrant *et al.* 2016). They congregate in huge numbers in the Snowy Mountains and elsewhere, attracting large numbers of indigenous Australians who used to collect the moths and roast them over hot ashes. They are said to be sweet and walnut-like in flavour, and very nutritious with high levels of protein. For the indigenous Australians, these gatherings were an important part of their cultural traditions, a chance for different tribes to meet and an excellent opportunity for meeting future marriage partners. Some people still eat the moths – I would have liked to try one.[172] [173] A festival to celebrate the arrival of the moths is still held today, near Albury at Mungabareena Reserve, with indigenous performers, spear and boomerang throwing competitions and bush tucker. A few years ago, the name was changed from Bogong Moth Festival to the Ngan Girra Festival (which means 'gathering place'). Up to 5000 people – both locals and overseas visitors – come to the festival each year.

Unlike the Monarch, the Bogong moths fly at night, the same individual making both the forward and reverse journeys, flying to places that they have never previously visited and potentially using a variety of sensory cues to follow a genetically inherited pre-programed route and to stop at the correct destination. A possible trigger for migration is the change in day length which occurs during spring and autumn, a cue that could be tracked using a circadian clock, as proposed for Monarch butterflies. Spring moths have been recorded steadily flying south to southwest, while autumn moths were steadily aligned north to northeast, despite wind directions being much more variable, and the moths fly a few metres above ground even going upwind. They fly at night, when visual cues are dimmer and unreliable; it is currently unknown how the moon, stars and even the Milky Way[174] would be visible to the small compound eyes of the Bogong Moth, but they have been observed to maintain their flight direction even on completely overcast nights when all visual celestial compass cues are obscured.[175] This suggests that they might possess a magnetic compass sense for holding their migratory direction.

172. For cooking, take a generous handful of moths, 1 cup each of plain flour, self-raising flour and powdered milk, ¼ teaspoon raising agent and water. Then pound up the moths with the powdered milk and mix in the other ingredients, add water to make a stiff dough, shape into a flattened ball to about 2.5cm high, lightly flour the surface and cook until cooked through. Serve hot. (Recipe courtesy of Vic Cherikoff https://themountainjournal.wordpress.com/environment/bogong-moth/ accessed 10 April 2020).
173. However, it is important to be careful as it is possible to have an allergic reaction to moth wings; I experienced this myself when I swallowed some moth scales in my coffee and my face swelled up later like a balloon – the moth was not identified.
174. The passage of the Milky Way, the moon and stars across the sky from dusk to dawn would require moths to compensate for this movement during their nightlong migrations.
175. The African dung beetle *Scarabaeus zambesianus* is able to use celestial polarisation patterns (produced by the scattering of moonlight when it strikes tiny particles in the atmosphere) to orientate itself so that it can move along a straight line (Dacke *et al.* 2003). Other African dung beetles have been shown to orient to the starry sky (not to individual stars, but to the Milky Way) to move along straight paths (Dacke *et al.* 2013).

They might also assess the visual optic flow of landscape features on the ground below, helping them compensate for changes in wind direction, and perhaps this is one reason that they fly low down near the ground.[176] An obvious cue for these moths is the long and continuous ridge of the Great Dividing Range which runs just inland along the entire east coast of Australia; in the spring when the moths arrive the alpine peaks are still covered in snow, and even at night the snowfields would create a bright visual beacon unique to this part of the Great Dividing Range, especially if lit by the moon or stars. Other sensory cues the moths could use to signal their approaching alpine destination are barometric pressure and temperature, both of which decline with increasing elevation. Then as the first moths approached their final specific aestivation site (a cave or crevice in the high mountains), to precisely pinpoint their final destination, they would follow "the smell of the remains of dead bodies and excrement from countless generations of moths from previous years"[177] and subsequent moths would follow the "olfactory beacon" of the moths already there.

You can guess whether a moth is a regular migrant or not by looking at its wing shape. Moth species differ in their flight ability and design, so that those that regularly migrate long distances will be designed for longer flight, whilst those that stay in the same place will need their wings less and may focus energy away from flight and into reproduction and hence have longer and/or fatter bodies. This of course only applies to those species which are programmed to migrate, not unintentional migrant species. The design of flying animals is closely related to their ecology and behaviour (Wickman 1992). In particular, biomechanical design in Lepidoptera (e.g. the relative allocation of energy into body mass for reproduction or wing shape) affects flight performance (Fric, Klimova & Konvicka 2006) and Lepidoptera such as hawkmoths adapted for fast flight tend to have relatively narrow wings (Scoble 2002).

The aerodynamics of moth flight are complex and successful flight depends on a range of factors including wing flexibility, wing venation, thoracic muscles, temperature and energy provision to flight muscles, with an intense leading-edge vortex on the down-stroke providing extra lift (Ellington et al. 1996). Wing shape may vary according to the requirement for speed, duration, agility and manoeuvrability during long-distance dispersal, foraging, mate-location, predator-avoidance and finding oviposition sites.

Some species have both resident and migrant populations. Monarch butterflies are renowned for migrating long distances, but not all populations of Monarchs migrate. The largest population of Monarchs breeds in eastern North America and travels thousands of kilometres to and from overwintering grounds in central

---

176. Experiments with the Tobacco Budworm found that most male moths flying upwind towards a sex pheromone through a blank tube without any visual patterning became disoriented, whereas when the tube was patterned they maintained momentum against the wind (Vickers & Baker 1994).

177. Warrant et al. 2016.

Mexico; in contrast Monarch populations in tropical and subtropical regions tend to stay put and breed year-round. A smaller population in western North America migrates between the Rocky Mountains and the central California coast where they congregate in Eucalyptus groves. I have seen them here in the 1980s in thousands rather than millions, over-wintering near Santa Maria seeking shelter from the freezing northern winters. University researchers were tagging the butterflies with a white label on the forewing; to my mind, the butterflies when released flew with a slight lean. Each label had a contact address so that details of where the butterfly was found could be sent back to the university. The researchers were trying to work out where the butterflies went, hoping that some at least would be found by interested observers and returned by post to the university. It is thought that they fly down from their summer sites in the Rockies to winter here near the warm Californian coasts.

The migrant Monarchs tend to have longer wings than the resident populations (Lundmark 2010); for example, migrating Monarchs that fly down the east coast of America to Cuba have longer and narrower forewings wings than the butterflies that stay there (Dockx 2007).[178] In fact, the forewings of eastern migrants are significantly larger than those of western migrants, and both of these groups had larger forewings than non-migrant groups; the wings of eastern migrants were the most elongated (Lundmark 2010). It has been widely observed that the forewing of the migratory Monarch is on average more acuminate than that of non-migratory Monarch populations – a difference considered significant not only statistically, but also functionally with respect to long-distance flight performance (Vane-Wright, Fage & Huertas 2017).

In contrast, many of the geometrid moths have broad butterfly-like wings and flutter slowly about; they cannot fly fast. Flight may also be related to body size. Moths may have low wing loadings, i.e. where the wings are relatively large in relation to body mass; moths with low wing loadings have less mass to move per wing area (Rydell & Lancaster 2000) and may be more adapted for dispersal (Danthanarayana 1976). Moths with high wing loadings may be more sedentary and may invest more in reproduction as relative abdomen mass is high (Hill, Thomas & Lewis 1999). This is true of Sandhill Rustics in Cornwall where in a narrow coastal environment female moths have the smallest wings in relation to body length of all the different subspecies, suggesting a greater investment in reproduction (Spalding 2013). Females have a lower forewing area/body length ratio than males and fly less, spending a large proportion of their time either resting motionless on grass stems or walking across the sand to find suitable grasses on which to lay their eggs (Spalding 2015). The nominate subspecies of the Sandhill Rustic *Luperina nickerlii nickerlii* is more mobile and has occasionally been found (e.g. in Alderney and Le Val-St-Père in Normandy) far from known populations (Lepertel & Quinette 2016), indicating an occasional ability to migrate; it has

178. This is true for birds as well where migrants tend to have wingtips that are relatively more pointed and more convex; they also have wings of relatively larger aspect ratio (Lockwood, Swaddle & Rayner 1998).

a high forewing ratio (i.e. forewing length divided by forewing breadth) and a relatively short body which indicates an ability to fly fast.[179]

When a migrant butterfly or moth arrives, we can estimate where they have come from by back-tracking using wind maps. The Painted Lady uses high-altitude winds to aid migration; spring abundance in northern Spain can be linked to populations in north Africa on the basis of wind patterns and back-trajectories calculated backwards to the probable source population (Stefanescu, Alarcón & Àvila 2007). These winds from north Africa often bring quantities of red dust which can coat the shiny surface of cars and windows.[180] If you see this you know that there is a possibility of rare migrants in the moth trap and it is time to put the moth lights out – some people just trap in their garden, others drive to well-known costal sites such as Portland Bill or Kynance Cove. There is a good chance that you can bag several migrant species, from common species such as Silver Y to rare species new to the UK.

So the same winds bringing over Silver Ys may also bring over extreme rarities such as the Boathouse Gem. This was first recorded in Britain in November 2014 by my friend and moth expert Mark Tunmore at his home on the Lizard peninsula (Tunmore 2015). It occurs on the north coast of the Mediterranean from Portugal eastwards as far as Taiwan, Japan and China; back-tracking weather maps showed that at the time of capture the weather was high pressure over the Mediterranean which meant that air was circulating northwards from Iberia and North Africa into southern Britain; the moth would have been carried on this airstream. As Mark points out – the most critical factor is probably luck.[181] The moth did not have an English name or a number.[182] It is bad form for the finder to name a moth; another moth expert should suggest a name, and the well-known moth expert David Brown suggested the name, based on the place of capture (the Boathouse) and the taxonomic closeness to other migrant Gem moths, such as the Tunbridge Wells Gem and the Scarce Bank Gem.

Another first for Britain was Patton's Tiger, first recorded on 29th May 2005 near Chichester. There are three theories as to its mode of arrival (Pratt 2020):

179. The hindwings are less critical for flight; Lepidoptera can still fly when their hindwings are cut off, although they lose manoeuverability and may be less able to avoid capture by bats (Jantzen & Eisner 2008).

180. I have been in a sandy dust storm in Fuerteventura (spring 2020) when it was hard to see more than 100 metres; the interesting thing was perhaps the colour of everything. The sand absorbs and scatters solar radiation entering Earth's atmosphere, reducing the amount reaching the surface, and absorbs long-wave radiation bouncing back up from the surface, re-emitting it in all directions. You can't see the sun but you can still burn as there are high levels of ultra-violet light; this might well have an effect on moth and butterfly activity as ultra-violet light is linked to their magnetic compass (e.g. Guerra, Gegear & Reppert 2014).

181. Note that another moth was illustrated under the same name caught in Devon on 28th October 2014 just beforehand and Mark thought that his "gold medal (would be) replaced with a silver one" – but this moth was wrongly illustrated and was in fact another species.

182. All British moths are allotted a number and fitted into taxonomic order – a new species has to have a new number (Agassiz, Heckford & Beavan 2015).

the individual was a part of a natural range extension, it occurred naturally as a wandering vagrant or it was an unnatural vagrant – perhaps a deliberate import. It is not thought to be migratory, being scarce in large parts of Europe where it only occurs on warm sandy sites in France and Germany and in habitats situated up to 2000m on high mountainous slopes in the Pyrenees, southern Alps and Appenines. However, further Patton's Tigers[183] turned up in Devon and the Isle of Wight and Davey (2006) calculated a meteorological backtrack trajectory which determined that potential for immigration existed from northern Spain, the Pyrenees and southern France two days prior to capture. Similarly, the first British record (in 2011) of the micro-moth *Euchromius ramburiellus* was back-tracked using meteorological charts which showed that at the date of capture winds were between south-east and south-west emanating from France, Iberia and North Africa (Johns *et al.* 2016).

It is useful to run moth traps in the winter months when most moth trappers have packed their moth traps away. It is in the winter that some of the rarest moths turn up, carried by the wind from their warm habitats in north Africa. It was on 26th December 2015 that I found a partially washed-out moth in my trap, inconspicuous against the grey egg boxes that I use to provide a resting place for captured moths. I did not recognise it so I pinned it for future examination. It turned out to be *Cornifrons ulceratalis*, a small greyish moth new to the UK (Parsons *et al.* 2016). At this time there were 16 recorded in England & Wales in December plus one in January 2016. It is widespread around the Mediterranean (Spain, Portugal, Italy, Greece and southern France) and abundant in parts of north Africa where it flies from October to May. It was probably lifted with sand particles and other insects within a thin ribbon of dust raised from the Sahara and carried to parts of southern England firstly on 16th December and again on 26th December (when I caught mine). Deep low-pressure systems were sweeping south-westerly winds into the UK during the warmest December since 1910. Modelling back trajectories using meteorological models[184] to identify possible source locations, including potential diurnal stopover points, pointed to source locations in Morocco or the Canary Islands (or both). These calculations were based on the following estimations, that:

- *Cornifrons ulceratalis* took off at local sunset time and landed at local sunrise time providing it was over land.
- If it was over water at sunrise it continued to fly until reaching land.
- Its flight speed equalled wind speed (i.e. it did not fly upwind).

183. Patton's Tiger was named by the finder after her father.
184. The most commonly used model is the HYSPLIT model (Hybrid Single Particle Lagrangian Integrated Trajectory Model) which is a system for computing simple air parcel trajectories, as well as complex transport, dispersion, chemical transformation and deposition simulations. A common application is a back trajectory analysis to determine the origin of air masses and establish source-receptor relationships and is used for example to track and forecast the release of radioactive material, wildfire smoke, windblown dust and pollutants from emission sources. The use for tracking moths is of minor value, unless used to track swarms of pest species. https://www.arl.noaa.gov/hysplit/hysplit/ accessed 21 April 2020).

- One of the moths may have stopped twice *en route* and the last leg might have been a flight of about 26 hours, and it probably arrived the day before being caught.

There is tremendous excitement in finding a new moth species for Britain, especially when it is named after you. Running my trap in my garden at Praze-an-Beeble on 22nd November 1995, I opened it up in the morning before going off to work. I didn't think there was anything at all in there. Putting the egg boxes back I noticed a grey noctuid moth hiding in one the dimples. Not recognizing it I put it in a box for later examination; it looked very like Shuttle-shaped Dart but was slightly different. It was *Agrotis herzogi* – new to Britain. My friend Gerry Tremewan (Editor of the *Entomologist's Gazette*) suggested that it be named Spalding's Dart and so it became. Someone suggested that it should be called the Oggy Pasty moth after the scientific name *herzogi* and the fact that it was found in Cornwall. Luckily this was ignored. At first it was not illustrated in the classic book by Bernard Skinner, as he declined to illustrate species that had only been recorded once in Britain, but a second was found on 17th December 2015 near a large B&Q hardware store at Poole in Dorset, presumably attracted to the artificial lighting. The moth is now illustrated in most moth books and it will undoubtedly be seen more often if entomologists run their traps in the winter. This name will live long after me.

Table 5.2. Named migrant species found in the UK, information from Martin Honey.

English name	Scientific name	Date discovered	Named after
Blair's Shoulder-knot	*Lithiphane leautieri hesperica*	1951	Kenneth Gloyne Blair*
Clancy's Rustic	*Caradrina kadenii*	2002	Sean Clancy
Dewick's Plusia	*Macdunnoughia confusa*	1951	A.J. Dewick
Dumeril's Rustic	*Luperina dumerilii*	1858	A.M.C. Dumeril
Eversmann's Rustic	*Actebia fennica*	1850	Eduard Friedrich Eversmann
Lorimer's Rustic	*Paradrina flavirena*	1967	R. Ian Lorimer
Patton's Tiger	*Hyphoraia testudinaria*	2005	S. Patton's father
Porter's Rustic	*Proxenus hospes*	1978	Jim Porter
Radford's Flame Shoulder	*Ochropleura leucogaster*	1983	J.T. Radford
Softly's Shoulder-knot	*Lithophane consocia*	2001	Raymond A. Softly
Spalding's Dart	*Agrotis herzogi*	22 Nov 1995	Adrian Spalding
Stephen's Gem	*Megalographa biloba*	1954	J.F. Stephens

*He named it the Stone Pinion, as it has rather dull greyish stone-like wings, but it soon became known as Blair's Shoulder-knot after the indistinct shoulder-knot marking at the base of the forewing (Owen 1985). Blair was also responsible for the discovery of two other moth species new to Britain: Blair's Wainscot (1945) and Blair's Mocha (1946).

Evidence suggests that both the abundance and diversity of immigrant moths arriving in Britain are increasing over time, probably due to climate change (Sparks, Roy & Dennis 2005) but perhaps also due to increased interest in moths. In 2003 I was asked with Mark Tunmore to carry out a feasibility study for the then forthcoming Macro-Moth Recording Scheme, now run as *Moths Count* by Butterfly Conservation (Spalding *et al*. 2005). As part of this exercise we sent out a questionnaire to moth recorders; a total of 1032 responses were received.[185] Amongst the questions, respondents were asked for the length of time they had been recording moths; out of the 907 respondents who answered this question, over 30% had been recording for less than four years. This indicated that there had been a surge of interest in the years leading up to this questionnaire, perhaps stimulated by the ready availability of field guides such as the then newly published guide by Waring & Townsend (2003). It was difficult to estimate from these figures how old the recorders were, but the four people who had been recording moths for over 70 years must have been well past pension age; some at least of the 538 people who had been recording for less than 10 years may have been fairly old, as many people take up moth recording after they retire.

Recent years have witnessed substantial influxes of scarce immigrants such as *Spoladea recurvalis*, *Antigastra catalaunalis*, Crimson Speckled and Small Marbled. Many, but not all, of our regular immigrants have increased in abundance, for example the Vestal showed a 925% increase in population levels over the period 1968–2007 (Fox *et al*. 2013). The Vestal is a beautiful moth, very variable in colour, with a rosy red or brown transverse stripe over a pale primrose yellow forewing. It can breed here but its survival depends on high temperatures. Huge numbers can be recorded in some years such as in 1947 and 1987; it can be flushed by trailing a rope between two people across a field (Pratt 2020), a technique also used for finding ground-nesting birds such as Snipe. Other migrant moths appear to have decreased in numbers, such as the Dark Sword-grass and Silver Y with 62% and 46% decreases respectively in population levels over the period 1968–2007 (Fox *et al*. 2103). Nevertheless, Silver Ys can still be seen in huge numbers. In the Fair Isles, it is an irregular breeder and abundant migrant subject to immense influxes. On moderate south-east winds on 6th August 1996 it was estimated on transect counts that half a million Silver Ys were seen passing north-westwards, and it was estimated that there were tens of millions in the whole of Shetland (Riddiford & Young 2017).

However, "the age of innocence" is gone (Vane-Wright, Fage & Huertas 2017). Commenting on the appearance of a Monarch butterfly on 6th July 2015 flying over the Palace Pier in Brighton, reported with a photograph on 9th July 2015 in the local newspaper *The Argus* under the banner headline "Monarch butterfly sighting in city centre results in a flutter of excitement", the authors write that "Unpopular though it will be with bird watchers and other 'romantic' naturalists keen to honour and

---

185. The results showed clearly that moth recording was largely a male-dominated activity, with women representing just 12.4% of the total numbers responding to the questionnaire.

respect the epic journeys these insects can make, in future to know any truth about them in Europe will require that they are collected, or at least handled long enough to get good photographs, and a tissue sample for DNA." Had a Monarch been seen in England almost any time before 1980, excitement about its possible flight from the Atlantic Islands, or even North America, would have been entirely justified.[186] The authors go on to write:

According to Salmon (2000), of the 700 or so Monarchs reported from England in the period 1876–2000, "nearly two-thirds have been reported in the past twenty years". What could account for such a sharp rise since 1980? More active recording, including the use of electronic media for rapid communication, might be the only explanation necessary. Establishment of the butterfly in Spain during this period might be another. Climate change, perhaps. But is it just a coincidence that 1980 also marks the establishment of the butterfly house industry in Britain?[187]

In addition, the last 20 years or so have seen the establishment of the special event butterfly-release business. The increasing frequency of sightings of the Monarch flying free in the British Isles can be the result of at least six different sources (taken from Vane-Wright, Fage & Huertas 2017):

- Off-course migrant individuals arriving direct from north-eastern North America.
- Accidental wind-assisted flights from wild populations on the Atlantic Islands.
- Northerly movements from Spain.
- Escapees from butterfly houses.
- Accidental or deliberate release by hobbyists or individuals.[188]
- Deliberate release of butterflies bred especially for the 'butterfly occasions' trade.

Based on differences between the various populations the authors are almost certain the Brighton Monarch did not represent the migratory Monarch populations from North or Central America, nor the Atlantic Island or Spanish populations. It might instead have been derived from populations in Columbia or perhaps Ecuador. We are left with release from an event, or an escape from a hobbyist or butterfly house that used stock originating from somewhere in the northern half of South America. Thus, all records of Monarchs in Europe will become increasingly

186. A friend, when living on the Lizard, phoned me to say that he had seen a Monarch butterfly in his garden near Porthleven. I said I would drive right over, a journey of about 20 minutes and 8 miles, adding "please don't catch it – I want to see it in the wild." I drove fast through the Cornish lanes, and Robin met me at the gate. He led me into the house – and there was the butterfly in a pot. Definitely a Monarch, a spectacular butterfly – but no longer wild, but a captive. A butterfly flying in a pot is not the same as a butterfly flying free in its natural habitat.
187. Vane-Wright, Fage & Huertas (2017).
188. Many years ago I bred Camberwell Beauty butterflies in a netted cage; one day as I went into the cage a Camberwell Beauty floated out high above my head. A few days later a Camberwell Beauty was recorded at Lanhydrock 18 miles to the west. Was it the same butterfly?

debased as evidence of natural range change, or as environmental bio-indicators (cf. Pyle 2010).

Migrant species can elicit excitement and strong emotions. They show the uncertainty of nature and are beyond the control of man, beyond the control of Natural England and the wildlife non-governmental organisations such as the wildlife trusts, appearing randomly and unexpectedly. Occasionally events get out of hand. The arrival of a Green Darner on 9th September 1998 in the Cornwall Wildlife Trust reserve at Penlee Point was such a case (Pellow 1999). This dragonfly is abundant in North America where it regularly migrates southwards along the Canadian and New England coasts of northeastern North America (Corbet 2000). One was probably carried on winds into Cornwall from Canada and was the first record for Europe. The news flashed on the dragonfly grapevine and enthusiasts flocked to see it. One of these was the international expert Philip Corbet who wanted to know to which subspecies the individual belonged. He obtained permission from the wildlife trust to collect and examine the dragonfly as a voucher specimen for the Natural History Museum. However, he was prevented from collecting the specimen by local naturalists and people who had travelled a long way to see it – Corbet called them vigilantes (Corbet 2000) and there followed an email campaign against him. Who was right? Threats of physical violence are never justified, but collecting a specimen when people are travelling to see it might be considered as unjustified. What takes precedence – the scientific desire to confirm the taxonomic status and preserve the specimen for posterity or the public thrill of seeing a new species for Britain; scientific knowledge or public enjoyment?[189]

One man's migrant is another man's pest species. The Small Mottled Willow is a major agricultural pest across the world; also called the Beet Armyworm, Asparagus Fern, Lesser Armyworm, Lesser Cottonworm, Lucerne Armyworm, Onion Armyworm and Sugarbeet Armyworm[190] it occurs as a serious pest of vegetable, field and flower crops. Susceptible vegetable crops listed[191] include alfalfa, asparagus, bean, beet, broccoli, cabbage, cauliflower, celery, chickpea, corn, cowpea, eggplant, lettuce, onion, pea, peanut, pepper, potato, radish, sorghum, soybean, spinach, sugarbeet, sweet potato, tobacco, tomato and turnip. The farmer does not want to see it; in the UK the mother delights in seeing it as it means that the winds are favourable and more migrant moths might turn up.

Other moths may be less welcome. *The Sun* used the Diamond-backed Moth *Plutella xylostella* to back Brexit with the 15th June 2016 headline: TIME TO MOTHBALL THE EU – NASTY EURO MOTHS HIT UK (VOTE LEAF TO PROTECT OUR COUNTRY … AND OUR CABBAGES). The article went on

189. I think if it had been me I would have collected the specimen after everyone had gone home and pretended the specimen had been eaten by the local cat, as happened to the Wilson's Warbler under a mile away.

190. https://gd.eppo.int/taxon/LAPHEG accessed 28 April 2020.

191. http://entnemdept.ufl.edu/creatures/veg/leaf/beet_armyworm.htm accessed 28 April 2020.

to say that Britain's cabbages may be annihilated by a massive swarm of tens of millions of these "super-moths" from Europe, which formed clouds two miles wide, and quoted one motorist as saying it was like "driving through rain".

CHAPTER 6. SPECIES IN THE INDUSTRIAL LANDSCAPE

Here we consider how wild species adapt to a man-made landscape, how they move in and around without man's help or hindrance. We see the Peregrine nest on the Civic Centre in the middle of Plymouth, not because someone has placed a Peregrine box there but because to the Peregrine it is a safe place to perch, reminiscent of its cliff-side home. These are species in charge of their own destinies, in man-made landscapes due to their own movement, there in spite of not because of man. Awareness of the development of the wildlife of a place as it has changed over centuries and been modified by man's activity constructs our 'moral geography' of the countryside and emphasises our part within it. The presence of certain key species gives a site a cultural importance and contributes to our 'sense of place', a sense of continuity with our industrial past, with the work of man in previous years. Too often, we see wildlife, particularly animals, as there despite us, when in most cases it is there because of us, the numbers and distribution of species being indirectly influenced by our activities, both past and present. The wildlife forms part of the history of a site, and the presence of particular species gives us clues as to how a habitat has developed and changed over the years; in Cornwall for example, everywhere has a long history, from Neolithic clearances on Bodmin Moor, to medieval tin-streaming sites, to china clay extraction in the St Austell district, to deep mining in the Camborne-Redruth district (Spalding 1996). The species here are not what I call "*McDonald's* species" – species out of context, with no natural historical connection with a site – but species here of their own volition, in their own right, the presence of which tells us something about the character and history of the site. These are the species which take over after Man has left, which show that Nature has triumphed – and will triumph in the end.

Mine sites

The abandoned metalliferous mine sites of Cornwall are historic signs of the time in the 18th and 19th centuries when Cornwall was world famous for mining for copper, tin, arsenic and lead.[192] The development of wildlife communities in Cornwall over several centuries was at least partly characterised by the loss of woodland (as trees were felled for charcoal furnaces and later for timber props for the mines) and by the consequent increase of heathland on thin acid soils to take the place of the lost trees (Bere 1982). These sites occur throughout Cornwall, covering over 3000ha (Spalding & Dinsdale 2000) and making an important contribution to Cornwall's nature-conservation resource (Spalding 1996).

The nature of the land when mining ceased has greatly influenced vegetation development and colonisation by wildlife (e.g. Bradshaw & Chadwick 1980). Nitrogen and phosphorus availability is low and pH values are generally very acidic, within the range of 4–5 (Whitbread-Abrutat 1995), and in places soils and associated micro-organisms are absent (Witter, Giller & McGrath 1994). Many of the sites are contaminated by metals. Work by researchers at the Camborne

---

192. The last working mine was South Crofty, worked for tin until 1998, although there are ongoing attempts to reopen it.

School of Mines has shown that contamination is patchy, with 'hot spots' of metals often associated with bare ground. Contamination is in the form of primary waste (residual unworked minerals on waste dumps) or processing waste (arsenic and other metal sulphides, found near the dressing floors, and concentrations of arsenic, cadmium and other minerals in the calciner flues, where ores were roasted to remove impurities). Analysis of sandy soil from four adjacent sites at Binner Downs near Leedstown in Cornwall showed low pH values and high metal contamination from arsenic, lead, copper and zinc, with lower levels of a suite of other metals such as cadmium, chromium, mercury, selenium and nickel (Spalding, Collins & Haes 2008). These areas are free of vegetation and solitary bees and wasps nest in the ground on south-facing banks where the soil is deep and soft enough for nesting but firm enough for nests to survive heavy rain; particle size analysis at some sites indicated that the soils where bees and wasps nest are very fine, with 84% of the particles less than 250μm.[193]

Heathland is often the dominant habitat on nutrient-poor soils. Ling is the commonest heather, forming a climax self-regulating community on toxic ground which inhibits the growth of competing plants. The tolerance of heavy-metal contamination (e.g. arsenic) by Ling may be due to the presence of mycorrhizal fungi, which reduces exposure of the host plant to metals; at some sites Ling grows in areas despite heavy concentrations of arsenic. Ling is important as a larval foodplant for a range of invertebrates and provides architectural structure for concealment and nesting places, but perhaps it is most important as a nectar source in autumn, when the mine sites are alive with flying insects.

A good example of an abandoned mine is Great Wheal Busy near Chacewater. It was worked periodically from about 1700 until the early 1900s, producing first 100,000 tons of copper ore, then tin and more recently 27,000 tons of arsenic. It was the first Cornish mine with a James Watt pumping engine (erected in 1778). On the face of it, then, these sites would appear to be inimical to wildlife – and indeed in the 1980s there was a movement to reduce metal contamination and plant with trees and cover with grass. In a brief study of Wheal Busy by me and my friend Chris Haes, we discovered 77 invertebrate species here, including Beautiful Yellow Underwing, Mottled Grasshopper, Heather Leafhopper, Sand Wasp, Heath Bumblebee, Common Colletes, Green Tiger Beetle and Heather Beetle. The Scarce Blue-tailed Damselfly has been recorded mating by the shallow unvegetated pools. Of special interest here is the tiny colony of Silver-studded Blue; despite being surrounded by extensive tracts of Ling and Bell Heather, at Wheal Busy it lays its eggs solely on Common Birds Foot Trefoil, which occurs in mats in places surrounded by scrub.[194]

---

193. Microns – 1 micron = 0.001mm.

194. The ants here are the Black Garden Ant, but colonies are very small and scarce in the shallow mine soils and may be one reason why Silver-studded Blue colonies tend to be small on these mine sites compared to the sand dunes where there are huge populations of *Lasius alienus*. The Silver-studded Blue larvae form a close relationship with these ants and spend much of their time within the ant nests.

These sites are important for a range of species. There is a correlation between bare ground on the one hand and the presence of arsenic, zinc, copper and lead. Bare ground is important for many invertebrates that require hot substrates; ground temperatures can rise to as high as 40°C. Many insects take special advantage of the lack of vegetation and the compacted, toxic dark-coloured soil which warms up quickly in the sun, using such areas for nesting, thermo-regulation and catching prey (Fry & Lonsdale 1991). Green Tiger Beetles are common on these sites. The larvae live in holes open to the sky; they wait for small creatures to fall in and eat them.[195] The Tiger Beetle Wasp parasitises the Green Tiger Beetle larvae. I have found with Chris Haes the wingless female at Wheal Busy; they find a larva, sting it to immobilise it and then lay a single egg on it.[196] In contrast, heavy metal pollution can be detrimental to many insects such as the Red Mason Bee which collects pollen and nectar from a range of sources; where these have heavy metal concentration there is a steady decrease in the number of brood cells constructed by females and an increase in the proportion of dead offspring so that the detrimental effects of heavy metal pollution may severely impact wild bee communities (Moroń *et al*. 2014).

These sites are especially important for the formation of communities where plants are found in unusual associations. These plants can be classified variously as absolute metallophytes (found on metal-rich soils only), local metallophytes (found on metal-rich soil only within a given region) or pseudometallophytes (widespread species occurring on both metal-rich and more normal soils as distinct races or ecotypes) (DoE 1994). They possess biological mechanisms which enable them to tolerate high levels of metals which are ordinarily toxic to plants. Some metallophytes have mechanisms to limit metal uptake, whilst others (hyperaccumulating plants) can amass high concentrations of metals in their tissues without symptoms of toxicity (Whiting, Reeves & Baker 2002). Hyperaccumulation may be a defence strategy to deter insects and prevent other plants from growing nearby, e.g. the Chinese Brake Fern can accumulate up to 27,000 mg kg-1 dry weight of arsenic from the soil into its above-ground biomass and it is possible that it uses this arsenic to deter invertebrate threat and plant competition (Jaffe, Ketterer & Smith 2018).[197] The evolution of tolerance of metal contamination can be extremely rapid in some cases (Macnair 1987a).[198]

---

195. To find out if a hole is occupied, put a small grass stem into the hole; if it comes out easily there is nothing inside; if it sticks, a Green Tiger Beetle larva has grabbed it and is trying to pull you in!
196. https://www.bwars.com/wasp/tiphiidae/methochinae/methocha-articulata accessed 5 May 2020.
197. The plants accumulate arsenic in their leaves, and these drop from the plant back into the top layer of soil increasing arsenic accumulation here and preventing other plants which are intolerant of arsenic to grow here. The threat to insects is less clear because in their research increasing arsenic decreased the total abundance and richness of invertebrates but the effect was varied across different insect groups (Jaffe, Ketterer & Smith 2018).
198. Metallophytes can be used as bio-indicators (indicating where metalliferous substrates occur), for ecological restoration (e.g. using metal-tolerant grasses for reseeding areas) or for metal recovery (harvesting toxic metals from polluted sites with hyperaccumulating plants) (Whiting, Reeves & Baker 2002).

In Cornwall, Thrift is a local metallophyte, associated particularly with copper mine wastes, but more typically a coastal plant. Some of the most extensive colonies in Cornwall are associated with saltmarsh vegetation in estuaries contaminated by mine run-off (Jenkin et al. 1996). There are also extensive areas of Thrift growing inland, such as in Poldice Valley, the vegetation reminiscent of coastal cliffs but five miles from the nearest sea. Common Bent grass is a pseudometallophyte common on some of these sites, where it appears to have become tolerant of metal contamination; in some areas it is the commonest grass. On mine sites in Devon, Macnair (1987b) found that Common Bent collected at Wheal Exmouth was tolerant of lead and copper and samples collected at Devon Great Consols were tolerant of arsenic and copper (but not lead or zinc), whereas specimens collected on uncontaminated grass pasture showed no tolerance of any metal. The absolute metallophyte liverworts Greater Copperwort and Lesser Copperwort and the mosses Scopelophila cataractae and Cornish Path Moss are restricted to copper-contaminated substrates; their presence always indicates copper. Cornish Path Moss is endemic to Cornwall where it has only been found in three sites, one of which has been destroyed, and so is now only known from two sites in east Cornwall.[199] Even woodlice can serve as bio-indicators of metal pollution, although they need to be crushed and the metal content analysed (Hopkin & Hames 1994).

Other species are associated with abandoned pits and quarries (Spalding, Hartgroves, Macadam & Owens 2002). Peregrines grace the steep quarry slopes which form havens safe from dogs, foxes and people, specifically in china clay quarries. In these quarries, low lying areas form hot sheltered places with short flowery turf where insects can nectar out of the wind. The china clay substrate is not, unfortunately, generally of suitable structure and firmness for ground-nesting insects such as solitary bees. Perhaps the rarest coloniser of these areas is Western Rustwort which is associated with disused china clay pits where it grows as a colonist on unshaded or lightly shaded clay. It is threatened by shading from taller plants so active quarrying helps maintain the open disturbed habitat that it requires (Holyoak 2009). It is abundant here, as a thin purple/brown covering over china clay soils that have been undisturbed for several years. Its existence here presents an obstacle for the development of these sites for wind and solar farms, but it is easy to translocate under licence from Natural England.

High Speed One (HS1)
Other species make more direct use of man's industry. I worked for many years on the Channel Tunnel Rail Link (CTRL, now called HS1). To many people it is a scar on the countryside, resulting in the loss of ancient woodland and the cutting up of key habitats. To me, when I first visited with Catriona Neil before the trains were running, it was an exciting wildlife opportunity, forming a long wildlife

199. I was asked by Plantlife to give risk assessment advice on the management of one site in east Cornwall where the issue was having people on site on hands and knees using a hand lens doing survey work which would bring them into close contact with the soil and most especially exposure to arsenic.

corridor through the Kentish landscape along which wild species could travel and an opportunity for wildlife management to encourage species to colonise new areas. This was clear when we took a helicopter ride along the line from Folkestone north to Ebbsfleet; apart from the occasional bridge over the main roads, this was an unbroken vegetated habitat protected from the surrounding countryside along its entire length by high fences. It was apparent from the air that the main biodiversity feature centred on the extensive grasslands that run parallel to the track; these grasslands form a wildlife corridor joining key areas in the wider countryside, especially south of Ashford. North of Ashford, woodland is more common as a linking feature in the fragmented landscape and the HS1 links several SSSIs[200] and several ancient woodlands. In this section of the railway there are two land bridges – at Knights Place and Temple Wood near Strood – established especially for wildlife to cross the line without danger to wild animals or to the safe running of the railway. Recent scientific analysis has also shown that these high speed railways do not necessarily form a barrier to butterfly movements. Certainly, the Gatekeeper butterfly shows homing behaviour when released on the other side of a railway at a short distance from their capture site, with 30% crossing back over the railway; in an intensive agrarian landscape, railway verges can play a substitution habitat role for grassland butterflies (Vandevelde, Penone & Julliard 2012).

HS1 passes through the North Kent Plain, the North Downs and the Wealden Greensand, and at first the lineside provided new open bare ground habitat on both chalk and sand, ideal for new species to colonise, especially on warm south-facing sheltered slopes. Over several years we regularly monitored wildlife within the fence, from woodland plantings to Badger setts to nesting Skylarks; these areas are protected by security fencing from man and dogs and as such are havens for nesting birds, reptiles and other creatures.[201] The HS1 corridor is of high value for reptiles because there are extensive areas of open sandy soil, with an increasing food resource as the vegetation developed. High temperatures are especially beneficial for cold-blooded animals such as reptiles which heat themselves up in the sun before chasing prey. For example, Adders are most active between 10°C and 16°C, Grass Snakes sun-bask when the temperature is above 27°C and Common Lizards search for food when their body temperature reaches 30°C. These three species are common within the corridor, with Grass Snakes especially doing well near the balancing ponds. We set out 30 TinyTag TGX-3080 dataloggers 2cm below ground on south or west-facing banks in grassland along the entire length of the CTRL.[202] Mean temperatures throughout the corridor were fairly constant at 10–11°C for the year but the highest temperature recorded was 48°C, with 18

---

200. Three SSSIs overlap the HS1 corridor: Seabrook Stream SSSI, Cobham Woods SSSI and Shorne & Ashenbank SSSI.
201. We even found an abandoned Green Iguana, clinging to a rabbit fence; looking lost and cold, it was taken to the local RSPCA.
202. 30 data loggers synchronised to take temperature readings every four hours, so each datalogger takes six readings per day which equates to 2190 readings in a non-leap year, i.e. 65,700 readings for 30 dataloggers over a single year.

dataloggers recording temperatures over 30°C; the highest temperatures were on the eastern greensands near Folkestone.

The corridor is excellent for insects. With my friend Graham Collins, we discovered the ichneumon *Itoplectis viduata* – a species completely new to Britain – in May 2005, identified for us by Mark Shaw at the Royal Scottish Museum in Edinburgh where it is now on display. It probably parasitises the pupae of Burnet moths whilst in their cocoons, which are widespread and common along HS1. We also found the rare fly *Gymnosoma nitens* on 1st September 2004; it is a member of the Tachinidae family and in Essex is associated with post-industrial sites along the East Thames Corridor. It lays its eggs on the ground-dwelling Sand-runner Shieldbug which is locally distributed across southern England in brownfield sites, warm slopes on calcareous grassland and also sandy areas such as occur within the HS1 corridor. The conspicuous – and easily identifiable – Wasp Spider has become widespread and common here; this species feeds on grasshoppers and other insects and requires areas of longer grassland both for web-creation and for its prey. It is a relative newcomer to Britain, having been first recorded in Britain in 1922 at Rye but has now spread through suitable habitat in southern England, even occasionally being reported as far west as Cornwall. The rare micro-moth *Stigmella aceris*[203], which feeds on Field Maple, has been found in the planted plots – but not in sufficient numbers to seriously harm the plants. The presence of a rare species on a planted tree presents an interesting dilemma; we suggested that provided no evidence of serious harm to the planted Field Maple is found, this rare moth should be allowed to survive here. We also found the Chalkhill Blue butterfly within the corridor near the North Downs Tunnel.

The Small Ranunculus was another species recorded here, probably feeding on Prickly Lettuce, which was common in waste areas along the rail corridor; formerly a relatively common species in the south-east, it had become extinct by 1939 but became re-established from about 1997 in Kent and Essex and has since spread north and west. The newly disturbed ground within the rail corridor presented an ideal resource for this species to colonise and move northwards through Kent. Another recent invader, the Horse Chestnut leaf-miner Moth, which has spread into Britain since 2002 from northern Greece, occurred in huge numbers; I estimated over 27,000 individual moths on the bark of one of the old Horse Chestnuts that occurred at Eyhorne Street (the larvae feed within the leaves and can cover almost the whole tree but, despite the large numbers found on individual trees, there appears to be no evidence that permanent damage is caused).

Marjoram was planted in several plots between Fawkham Junction and the southern end of the North Downs Tunnel. This is the foodplant of the rare Black-veined Moth, which lays its eggs on grasses and flower heads from which the caterpillars move to feed on Marjoram (and possibly other plants). Several of these sites are likely to be suitable for the Black-veined Moth. The HS1 corridor provides

---

203. Called by some the Scarce Maple Pigmy.

a link between several historic and current sites and with suitable management the HS1 could have been a pathway along which this lovely day-flying moth could fly between sites.[204]

HS1 was (and perhaps still is) also home to the Grey Mouse-ear. It is an inconspicuous low-growing plant only about only 2–3cm high growing in sparsely vegetated areas. It is a winter annual which germinates in October and November and flowers in April and May. The flowers self-pollinate, and seed is set after May; it requires open ground in which the seeds can germinate and grow as they cannot compete with dense grass or vegetation. In the UK it is known only from Kent and Bedfordshire; in Bedfordshire it occurs on a railway embankment in the Sharnbrook Summit nature reserve. It is associated with railways and may have been accidentally introduced to Britain, although the Kent populations could be native since they pre-date the construction of HS1. In Kent, it now probably only occurs within the rail corridor, although it may be still be present in the Longfield Chalk Bank nature reserve. A population was set up immediately outside the railway fence where it occurred on ant hills formed by the Yellow Meadow Ant. These ant hills provided the main areas of open ground on the site; however, the site was left un-managed and the Grey Mouse-ear was crowded out by more vigorous vegetation.

Early spring dry weather is probably beneficial to Grey Mouse-ear as it restricts the growth of other potentially competing plants. Within the fence, we estimated in 2011 that the total number of plants present was about 5000 plants, up from 4000 in 2008. One of the key factors influencing its survival was the amount of bare ground; when we finally left the railway management team, bare ground here was down to about 25% and it is doubtful that the plant still survives there. Many of the plants were struggling against vigorous Oxe-eye Daisy which dwarfs the tiny Grey Mouse-ear. Other plants such as Red Fescue, Common Bird's-foot Trefoil and Salad Burnet were growing vigorously on the bank, reducing the amount of bare ground. Other impacts on Grey Mouse-ear included nutrient enrichment (probably in part associated with the growth of White Clover, as shown by the invasive Common Nettle at the top of the embankment), scrub encroachment (e.g. by Buddleia) and non-native invasive plants (e.g. Garden Bellflower) moving in. The site was very difficult to survey as it formed a narrow strip at the top of a steep cutting; one slip and you would be falling down onto the railway and there would be no escape from the trains travelling at over 200km an hour.

We recorded several orchids within the rail corridor, including Greater Butterfly Orchid, Common Spotted Orchid, Pyramidal Orchid, Southern Marsh Orchid and several Bee Orchid. Common Broomrape, a parasitic plant without chlorophyll, was found to be abundant in plots south of the North Downs Tunnel, where it is associated with clovers.

---

204. This idea was considered and approved by Natural England but was eventually dropped, perhaps as a result of changes in railway management.

The classic railway[205] also provides a home for several wildlife species. The Large Blue butterfly has naturally colonised railway cuttings in Somerset, spreading along the rail corridor from the introduction site at Green Down. The steep cuttings have provided hot sheltered habitat where the associated red ants *Myrmica sabuleti* can thrive.[206] Steep west-facing cuttings at Saunderton provide sheltered habitat for the Duke of Burgundy butterfly, where they fly down from the adjacent habitat to lay eggs on Cowslip, preferring the areas where the railway men have cleared scrub and made open glades, a by-product of the process of removing trees that in autumn shed leaves on the line, causing train wheels to slip.[207] There are at least nine colonies of the rare Black Hairstreak butterfly along railways. They occur, for example, at Rushbeds SSSI, where I worked in 2010 with Network Rail and Cleartrack to manage the rail corridor for wildlife – for Grass Snake, Butterfly Orchid, Twayblade, Wood Mice (as indicated by gnawed nuts), Dragon's Teeth, Marbled White and Brown Hairstreak. In particular, we cleared Hawthorn and Bramble that created shade where the Black Hairstreak flies amongst the tall sunny sheltered banks of Blackthorn. These areas also contained abundant Cowslip, and, although the Duke of Burgundy had disappeared from the site, by cutting the grass and raking off the arisings we ensured that the site was once again suitable for natural recolonisation by this rare and beautiful species.

The Fiery Clearwing moth occurs in the sidings at Dover; I have counted under licence the tiny black eggs on the leaves and stems of Curled Dock growing in the stony ballast here at the railway's edge, wearing my orange high viz clothing so that I can be seen from the passing trains. The Fiery Clearwing is well-protected in these areas, as the railway is securely fenced and patrolled, and access is strictly controlled; this moth is protected by law and when it was put on the protected list in 1998 – but before the legislation came into effect – several moth collectors rushed down to Dover and Folkestone to collect it from the cliffs.

Butterflies and roads
It has been recognised for over thirty years that roads can be important for wildlife including butterflies, with 25 of the 60 British butterfly species recorded on roadside verges (Way 1977). Most of these species occupy the grassland habitat present along the roadside verges or central reservations especially where the verge has been undisturbed for many years. In some cases, particularly in intensively farmed landscapes, roadside habitats may provide the best chance of seeing butterflies in the area, usually the more mobile species such as Red

205. The railway outside the high speed areas.
206. I have walked these lines with Dave Simcox, the Project Officer for the Large Blue Project, looking for Large Blues. The lines are dangerous, especially in cuttings and along curves where there are no safe refuges. We had railway men with us, a COSS (Controller of Site Safety) and two lookouts; they started off very dismissive of butterflies but became fascinated as the project progressed and one started finding thyme plants for us. We had to abandon the attempt to visit one area as there was no place of safety to get to if a train came – the only escape was to jump onto a steep bramble-covered slope.
207. Leaves on the line are a real problem in cuttings where they can pile up in rotting heaps; I have known trains unable to stop at railway stations due to slippage. On embankments and in open countryside leaves dry out and are blown away in the wind.

Admiral and Small White (Munguira & Thomas 1992), but rare species can also be found including Adonis Blue, Black Hairstreak, Brown Hairstreak, Chalkhill Blue, Chequered Skipper, Dingy Skipper, Grizzled Skipper and Lulworth Skipper (Thomas, Snazell & Ward 2002).

A pioneer study (Feltwell & Philp 1980), in what was claimed to be the first general study of the natural history of an entire motorway in Britain, found that the M20 motorway verges (the central reservation was not studied in the interest of safety) were important for butterflies, with 16 species recorded including large colonies of Essex Skipper, Marbled White and Ringlet. Roads are known to be especially important for butterflies associated with early successional habitat, e.g. short-turf grassland with abundant bare ground (Morris *et al*. 1994) and it is often these species (e.g. Silver-spotted Skipper) which are most under threat today. Additional habitat suitable for butterflies and associated with roads includes woodland, bracken scrub, heathland and boundary features. Although roads may be considered harmful to wildlife since they may reduce connectivity and create a significant barrier to the movement of wildlife species within landscapes (Mader 1984), roads built through intensive farmland, urban areas and other poor biotopes are likely to result in a net gain for insect diversity (Thomas, Snazell & Ward 2002). Studies in France along new motorways have shown that three species of Burnet moth have significantly expanded their range due to natural colonisation of new roadside embankments (Faillie & Nicolle 2003). Potential positive effects of roads on butterflies include (Spalding 2005):

- The provision of additional wildlife habitats in intensively farmed agricultural landscapes; the greatest abundance of butterflies in intensively farmed or urban land landscapes may be found besides roads (Munguira & Thomas 1992) where the verges act as wildlife refuges.
- The provision of wildlife corridors in fragmented landscapes; many butterfly species are reluctant to cross intensive farmland; for example Gatekeeper and Meadow Brown showed limited movement across intensively farmed agricultural landscape (4.7% and 16% respectively) in a study by Dover (1991) and instead may move along roads as wildlife corridors linking isolated areas of nature conservation value.
- The provision of stepping stone habitat; this is particularly important for those butterflies which occupy a metapopulation structure. Maximum natural single-step colonisation distances are different for each species; they have been calculated for some of the rarer butterflies, e.g. 0.6–1km for Silver-studded Blue and 1.4km for Black Hairstreak (Thomas, Thomas & Warren 1992). The smaller the gap between habitat patches the quicker the vacant patch can be colonised.
- Protection from predators in the central reservations; these may provide an important safety refuge for invertebrates from those predators which are unable to cross the road (Port & Thompson 1980).

Light pollution

Although we have seen how some species can colonise new urban or industrial habitat, there is one area where wildlife is slow to respond to changes to the countryside and the spread of urbanisation. I am lucky enough to live in a dark area of Cornwall where at night I can see the stars from my garden, and I can walk across Loe Bar at night looking for Sandhill Rustic moths under the stars.[208] In contrast, about one fifth of the world population live in areas where the Milky Way is no longer visible to the naked eye (Cinzano, Falchi & Elvidge 2001) and much of mainland Britain is brightly lit at night.[209] Recent global surveys of night sky brightness have concluded that 23% of land surfaces between 75°N and 60°S, including 88% of Europe and 47% of the United States, experience nightly "light pollution" in the form of an increase in night sky brightness at least 8% above the natural level (Falchi *et al.* 2016). People are wary of the dark; you can see perfectly well at night especially if there is a moon, but you need to wait until your eyes can adapt to the dark.[210] Go out without a torch in summer and you might see phosphorescence in the still summer estuaries of south Devon and Cornwall, but you must wait until it is completely dark – then stir the water to see the sparkling algae or scoop the sparks up in your hands and let them run sparkling down your arms, or swim amongst the flashing phosphorescent stars. On tropical beaches you can run along the night wet sand and leave behind phosphorescent footsteps. You won't see this under street lights. The stronger the lighting in a street the darker seem the unlit areas. We have changed the world with lights. It has even been shown that urban lighting is one of the reasons along with higher temperatures that trees (Oak, Beech, Ash, Sycamore) burst their buds earlier in cities than in the darker countryside (ffrench-Constant *et al.* 2016). As a sign that we have lost that intimate connection with our natural environment, there is a social drive to insist on installing lights everywhere; local planning authorities follow recommendations from the police that all dark corners are lit so that crime cannot flourish there.

Ambient light level is one of the strongest factors driving animal behaviour (as we can see when we run a moth trap). This is even true for light adverse species such as bats and hedgehogs. Most organisms have evolved for millions of years under natural cycles of light and dark and a substantial proportion of life is nocturnal (30% of all vertebrates and >60% of all invertebrates) (Hölker *et al.* 2010). Adverse effects for wildlife come from direct lighting and from sky glow[211],

---

208. My neighbour, however, wanted the council to install street lighting, so that drivers can slow down when they see one of her cats running across the road.
209. See https://www.nightblight.cpre.org.uk/maps/
210. When I was at college in the late 1960s I decided to go home to see my parents in Hingham in Norfolk. I got out of the train at Dereham. The train was late, there were no taxis (and I could not have afforded one anyway) and no working phone box (and of course no mobile phones). There was nothing to do but to walk the nine miles home, even though I did not know the way. The sky was cloudy with no moon. I set out wondering whether it was the best thing to do. As I walked, my eyes grew accustomed to the dark and at crossroads I could read the finger signs pointing to Hingham. I was very relieved when I arrived home and banged on the door – my parents weren't as they were fast asleep.
211. The overall coverage by sky glow is nearly ¼ of global land area.

which may obscure the Milky Way which is used for orientation by many species (Gaston 2018). Compared to the slow evolution of wildlife, and for example the separation of the Lepidoptera from the Trichoptera over 200 million years ago, the impact of lighting everywhere is of recent origin, dating back to the use of gas street lighting in the early 19th century and later – more radically – to the invention of the incandescent filament light bulb in the late 19th century. We have had electric street light for less than 140 years, no time at all for wildlife to adapt. We are just beginning to understand how many species are affected by lights.[212]

The Glow-worm is a widespread species, found from Portugal and Britain in the west to China in the east and almost as far north as the Arctic Circle (Tyler 1994) so is able to survive in a wide range of habitats. In Britain it occurs widely in Scotland, and my brother Julian has found it at 140m above sea level near Galashiels and I have found it in open coniferous woodland near Canillo in Andorra at about 1300m above sea level. All stages glow with a soft green light but the brightest lights are from the wingless females which climb up stems in open grassy areas where they use the light to attract flying males.[213] It is still possible to collect glow-worms – as I did once – place them in a jar and read a book by their light.[214] They wait until it is dark, in England usually about one hour after dusk, when ambient light levels fall below 1.3 lux, before emitting the light at the end of the abdomen; bright lights stop their display and they are never active above 15 lux (Dreisig 1975). Their larvae appear to be most active – or at least most likely to emit light – during the new moon phase of the lunar cycle, i.e. larval activity seems to be intrinsically synchronised to the mechanical lunar cycle (Gunn & Gunn 2012). Males are attracted to light traps that emit yellow-green light (De Cock 2009) and also attracted to low-pressure sodium street lamps (Owens & Lewis 2018). They can be attracted to the green indicator light on a generator.[215] High-pressure sodium lights interfere with courtship communication (Hopkins *et al.* 2015) which means that the females are less successful in their mating strategy when near these street lamps. I remember them many years ago in large numbers in Surrey near Dorking and on the Cornish coastal cliffs and sand dunes; now they are much reduced in numbers although still widespread. In the *Poldark* novels by Winston Graham (based on Cornwall around 1800) Demelza walked at night with glow worms lighting her path[216]; this would be difficult now.

---

212. In Germany the orb-web spider *Larinioides sclopetarius* has moved from its natural habitat near water to set its webs close to lights in the urban landscape, occupying a vacant new man-made niche full of prey attracted by the lights (Reynolds 2019).
213. I used to live in a wooded valley near Liskeard. One night, sleeping with the window open, I awoke to find a soft green glow on my pillow. A male glow-worm had flown through the window. Until then, I did not realise that glow-worms lived in this valley.
214. In *The Grove of Eagles* by Graham (1963) he writes: "You can read by the light of three or four glow-worms."
215. My friend Tony Atkinson found 15 males clustered round a green generator light on Penhale Dunes in Cornwall on 22 July 2016.
216. Another mention by Graham (1946) is "An hour before dawn they went down to the cove, following the bubble of the stream and the descending combe, with a glowworm here and there green-lit like a jewel in the dark".

Light attracts wildlife. If you stand still at night in the forests of Sabah or Sarawak and allow your eyes to adjust to the dark you can see that it isn't dark anymore; as your eyes get accustomed to the dark you can see fungi and decaying leaves glowing all across the tropical forest floor – turn on your torch and the glow disappears. One theory as to why fungi glow is that they attract small invertebrates that then spread their spores as they travel across the forest floor (Sivinski 1981).

One of the best-known examples of lights attracting wildlife of course are the moths, although some moths exhibit negative phototaxis, e.g. the Mouse Moth which appears to scuttle away from light and is rarely caught in light traps. There are several theories for this (Nowinszky 2003). The main theories are as follows.

- Moths use natural light sources (the moon and stars) for navigation (Sotthibandhu & Baker 1979). There may be a relationship between the size of moths and their susceptibility to flight interference by moonlight, so that larger moths fly higher, are more strongly influenced by moonlight and less attracted to light traps on moonlit nights (Taylor 1986). When flying at night, moths may keep light rays always on the same facet of their eye, so their body always forms the same angle with the rays of light. For the moth, the moon is practically in the infinite, so the rays of light arriving from there are perceived as parallel. As long as the moth keeps the same angle to the rays of light, it will fly in a straight line. In contrast, artificial sources of light, much closer than the moon, do not appear to come from the infinite and the rays of light reaching the eyes are radial, so that when maintaining a steady angle to the light the moth flies round in ever decreasing circles (Baker & Sadovy 1978).

- Moths get dazzled by a bright light (Robinson & Robinson 1950). There is some support for this theory as, with a bright lamp, moths often appear to settle further way from the light source than when the lamp is dull. A variation on this theory is based on the fact that the compound eyes of moths adapt to increases in light intensity by movement of pigment within the eye. Hamdorf & Högland (1981) suggest that moths (e.g. Elephant Hawk-moth) are blinded by bright lights as the pigment within the eye expands in response to UV wavelengths, especially after exposure to wavelengths between 352 and 443nm. Dim ambient light is then absorbed by the screening pigment, and the animal flies towards the light which is the only light visible to the animal.

- The contrast between a lamp and its background enhances flight to light. A light trap in dark woodland may attract more moths than one in the open (e.g. Spalding & Parsons 2004). The zone of attraction to a light also increases with the contrast with a dark sky (Eisenbeis 2006).

- Moths and other insects (just like human beings) see a dark stripe around the bright light of the lamp and attempt to reach this stripe to escape the light (Hsiao 1973). These stripes are called Mach's Bands which appear at points of inflection in a luminance (or colour) gradient. They result from lateral inhibition, a neural process in the early stages of the visual pathways that enhance the retina visual system and the sharpness of edges. For example, where you have stripes of the same colour but in slightly different shades, the contrast between the edges of these stripes is exaggerated, as soon as they contact one another, by triggering edge-detection in the human visual system. They are illusory. The artist Georges Pierre Seurat in his 1884 oil painting *Une Baignade, Asnières* (held in the National Gallery) (https://en.wikipedia.org/wiki/Bathers_at_Asni%C3%A8resn) exaggerates the effect around a seated bather with darker paint to provide a gentle contrast with the river background. However, these bands are quite thin and are usually only seen when there is a gentle contrast between two colours; as a result, I have some doubts as to the validity of this theory.

- The structure of the moth eye facilitates attraction to ultra-violet light. It is well known that moths come to UV light, which is the basis for the success of the moth traps that so many of us use. Visible light has wavelengths ranging from 400 to 700nm whereas ultraviolet is an electromagnetic radiation with a wavelength from 10nm to 400nm, shorter than that of visible light but longer than X-rays. Van Langevelde *et al.* (2011) has shown that moths show a preference for short wavelength light below 400nm, and that the abundance and species richness of moths attracted to light reduces markedly above 600nm. The lenses in the compound eyes of moths (and butterflies) contain an array of nipple-shaped protuberances called corneal nipples. There are differences in the shape of these nipples between nocturnal and diurnal species (butterflies and some species of day-flying moth) with the lowest reflectance[217] and the greatest photon absorption under UV light[218], which is probably one reason why moths are attracted to UV as they would perceive such wavelengths more intensely than other wavelengths (Spalding *et al.* 2019).

Despite this, it has been shown that moths are beginning to adapt to changes in light intensity. Natural selection should favour individuals with a lower propensity to being attracted by light since this attraction has potentially adverse effects – lights draw moths away from their habitats, in some cases they get trapped within light fittings, they are vulnerable to predation by bats and birds, and the males are drawn away from the females with reduced chances of mating (Spalding 2019). Some moths have begun to change their behaviour; populations of the Small Ermine from urban areas with high, globally relevant levels of light pollution over several decades now show a significantly reduced (36% reduction for males and

217. Reflectance is greatest in visible light.
218. Especially for those species with the longest corneal nipples and with the least gap between them.

28% reduction for females) flight-to-light behaviour compared with populations of the same species from pristine dark-sky habitats (Altermatt & Ebert 2016). As a result, there may be less direct mortality from lights and a lower predation risk – and indeed flight might be less necessary to sustain populations in a crowded urban area and the reduced flight-to-light response may be caused by a decrease in overall mobility.[219] Are we on the way to separate races of urban and countryside moth species?

The Peppered Moth

The classic case of the Peppered Moth is a case in point. The Peppered Moth gets its English name from the scattered black dots over its white wings, like pepper on the white of an egg. During the 19th century, as the industrial landscape extended across the British countryside, trees began to lose their lichen cover and, as the factory chimneys pumped out smoke from the industrial furnaces, soot began to blacken the tree trunks and walls of the urban areas – and also downwind of these urban centres; in the countryside trees retained their lichen cover and where there were no lichens the trunks were light grey or brown, depending on tree species. Peppered Moths are nocturnal and spend their days resting on these surfaces. Normal pale Peppered Moths – the form *typica* – were cryptic on unpolluted trees or walls, especially where lichen covered; on blackened trunks and walls they were conspicuous, and more readily predated by birds. A previously unknown black form *carbonaria* appeared in a 10-year window centred around 1819 as a mutation (Hof *et al.* 2016), where the pepper has taken over and the white has disappeared; Hof *et al.* (2016) found 87 DNA differences between the black and pale moths bred in the laboratory and then tested whether each was present in the wider variety of white moths found in the wild until they could single out one specific mutation and date roughly when it appeared. This new dark *carbonaria* colouring gave the moths a much better chance of hiding during the day from hungry birds. Black moths were first spotted in numbers in 1848 and by around 1900 had almost completely replaced the light-coloured form in the Manchester region[220]; *typica* was still present but in very low frequencies in cities, but still the most common form in the countryside. After the introduction of clean air laws in 1956 (the Clean Air Act

219. On the other hand, the size of the eyes, the light receptors in the eyes or the information processing of perceived light might be altered. This is much less likely as evolutionary changes in behaviour are likely to be much more rapid than changes in physical structures.

220. *Carbonaria* never reached 100% because of constant migration into urban areas by *typica* from adjacent rural areas; instead the frequency of *carbonaria* was pretty constant at over 85%. Other moths also have melanic forms. The proportion of the melanic form of the Scalloped Hazel showed considerable variation in different areas, probably due to the sedentary nature of this moth, so that numbers depended more on its adaptation to the local environment rather than on the immigration of darker individuals from other areas; the frequency of the melanic form of the Pale Brindled Beauty moth lies somewhere between the Peppered Moth and the Scalloped Hazel as its mobility is somewhere between the two.

1956) the air gradually became cleaner with a concomitant reduction in pollution and the *carbonaria* form lost its cryptic nature: black moths could be more easily seen on the pale tree trunks; *typica* became more widespread again. There was a lag between the reduction in pollution levels and the decline in *carbonaria* as it took some years before the surface of trees that the Peppered Moths rest on lightened as a result of soot fallout washing off, with the production of new unpolluted growth and the growth of lichens on the new cleaner surfaces (Majerus 1998). The *carbonaria* form still occasionally occurs but rarely; an occasional one turns up in moth traps and I have only seen it once in Cornwall. This is a graphic example of rapid evolutionary change and, although it has been reversed, shows how species can naturally adapt to these new industrial landscapes and survive Man's attempts at polluting the landscape. It is possible, according to Majerus (1998), that we only have about two decades until *carbonaria* has gone from the UK.

Wildlife will move into sites as Man leaves. An example is the return of Buzzards to Hampstead Heath in May 2020 as the covid-19 lockdown drastically reduced the number of visitors to the Heath. A similar effect happened at Penhale Dunes during the foot and mouth epidemic when the closure of the dunes to the public (and their dogs) led to an increase in the number of Skylark territories. At Chernobyl, 25 years after the nuclear accident on 26th April 1986[221], the removal of humans, and the cessation of their associated activities, has led to the exclusion zone becoming a thriving and biologically diverse environment with many protected species. Before the accident the pine forest represented a mature stable ecosystem. After the accident, high dose rates of ionizing radiation killed sensitive individual animals, altered reproduction rates, destroyed food resources and created new niches for colonising species. After time, stress was reduced and the ecosystem gained stability, but with different habitats available for wildlife – the pine forests had gone, grasslands and deciduous trees had established. However, one of the most abrupt and dramatic changes occurred when humans were removed from the area. 50,000 people were evacuated from the nearby town of Pripyat. Agriculture, forestry, hunting and fishing came to a halt. Animals fed on the abandoned cereal crops, potatoes and grasses. This and the hunting ban tended to compensate for the adverse biological effects of radiation. There was a significant increase in animal populations – Wild Boar, Red Deer, Roe Deer, Elk, Wolves, Foxes, Hares and Beavers – and in bird populations – Black Grouse and duck species. The exclusion zone has become a breeding area for White-Tailed Eagles, Spotted Eagles, Eagle Owls, Cranes and Black Storks. When humans are removed, nature flourishes. Wildlife returns as Man leaves, or adapts to changing conditions, some species becoming more common, others rarer. Man's interference affects our understanding and appreciation of these species and their ability to thrive in new landscapes despite Man's endeavours.

---

221. Environmental Consequences of the Chernobyl Accident and Their Remediation: Twenty Years of Experience. Report of The Chernobyl Forum Expert Group 'Environment'. International Atomic Energy Agency. Vienna, 2006.

CHAPTER 7. THE ARTIFICIALITY OF OUR UNDERSTANDING

What does an animal think when it looks at us? Michel de Montaigne in 1576 once considered: "When I play with my cat, who knows if I am not a pastime for her more than she is to me?"[222] What does a tiger think when it looks at its audience in the zoo? Does she think at all? Are we real to her? Frans de Waal wrote: "I regularly have this eerie impression that apes look right through me," he writes, "perhaps because they are not distracted by language." [223]

John Berger wrote in 2009 in *Why Look at Animals*: "That look between animal and man, which may have played a crucial role in the development of human society … has been extinguished." Does it matter, or does the way they see us make a difference to the way we see them? I went to see the Mark Dion *Theatre of the Natural World* exhibition at the Whitechapel Art Gallery in 2018. As part of it, he exhibited a colony of Zebra Finches in a large cage which was filled with the objects of their demise (traps, nets and guns) and a library of over 600 books on birds piled up on the branches of a tree at the centre of the cage – so that presumably the captive birds could see what they were called by Man. The birds ignored the books; as Dion wrote: "the absurdist conceit of a library for birds … their indifference to this human knowledge is rather striking." As Candy Stobbs, assistant curator at the gallery, wrote: "Is there any value in carefully organizing our relationship to the natural world if it is only to be blithely ignored by the fellow creatures who share it with us." The world is interpreted by humans and animals in different ways – as a heterogeneous multiplicity – and the birds refer to worlds that are located beyond our perception and perhaps remember earlier worlds outside the cage. It is Man who benefits from this connection, the birds are merely captive and outside our experience. Connecting with these birds helps us to define and explore the boundaries between us, and human identity and society. Dion writes: scientists "think and behave like they have a monopoly on what gets to be called nature"; we realise that other organisms see the world through different eyes. The exhibition aimed to offer the opportunity to re-think experimentally one's own identity and the relationship of human animals to other creatures.[224]

It could be said that, by capturing and displaying the Zebra Finches, Dion was treating the birds as captive possessions. The Chinese artist Huang Yong Ping tried to exhibit his *Theatre of the World* at the Guggenheim Museum in Bilbao in May 2018.[225] The exhibition featured two cages with live toads, snakes, lizards,

222. https://www.laphamsquarterly.org/animals/man-and-beast accessed 6 June 2020.
223. Quoted in the *New Statesman* 27 August 2016.
224. Identity is especially difficult when considering chimera, creatures derived from the parts of other animals in genetics (nowadays organisms that contain two or more different sets of DNA). We now have attempts at making human animal hybrids, where human organs are grown in pigs in order to provide transplant material, with fears of creating talking and thinking pigs; the question will be not "when is a pig too human" but "when is a human too porcine"? The resulting creatures, if they are living long, fit and healthy lives, untrammelled by failing bodies, are unlikely to be worried about the semantics. Professor John Harris quoted in the *Daily Telegraph* 6 June 2016.
225. https://www.youtube.com/watch?v=xHUoEWwfDjk accessed 20 May 2018.

cockroaches and other insects, all fighting for survival; the reptiles ate the insects. After protests by UdalBerri, a Bilbao protest group which said animals should be left in their natural habitats, and Paca, a Spanish animal rights group, which criticised the conversion of living beings into objects, the animals were withdrawn and the cages left empty. This perhaps represents the cultural differences between western Europe and China, but Huang Yong Ping strongly claimed to be part of the global contemporary art movement, not of China, and attributed the protests to the rise of conservatism. He wrote "An empty cage is not, by itself, reality. Reality is chaos inside calmness, violence under peace, and vice versa."[226] Thus, his art was transformed by public disquiet and ceased to be art. Similarly, the 2003 video work by Peng Yu and Sun Yuan *Dogs That Cannot Touch Each Other*, which showed four pairs of pit bulls facing each other on treadmills at opposite ends of the room and made to run at – but never reaching – each other, was at first staged at the Guggenheim Museum in New York but then closed due to public outcry. The Museum's response to criticism based on cruelty was: *We recognize that the work may be upsetting. The curators of the exhibition hope that viewers will consider why the artists produced it and what they may be saying about the social conditions of globalisation and the complex nature of the world we share*"[227] – which is as good a way as any of saying absolutely nothing.

The different views of wildlife between the two cultures was shown in the exhibition *A Case Study of Transference* by Xu Bing, a video where a boar and a sow covered in eastern and western symbols copulate in front of a crowd of people. The boar is covered with nonsensical English words, the other with fanciful Chinese characters as a satirical take on the collision of East and West, and as "a literal and visceral critique of Chinese artists' desire for enlightenment through Western cultural 'transference.'"[228] The boar in mating transfers his western understanding in a brutal way (the sow ignores the boar with her head in the straw). At one time, in response to complaints, the museum withdrew the video and instead displayed a blank monitor with an explanatory wall label. In this way, the label becomes more important than the art and the animals themselves are relegated to non-existent symbols that can mean whatever the viewer wishes; so the animal lover is happy that no animals are seen to be hurt, or viewed without their permission whilst having intimate connection with each other, and the artist is happy that the label explains his art and confirms his view that western views on animal welfare take precedence in the global art community.

Why have labels at all? Let the art connoisseur make up her own mind; let the animal lover make up his own mind; let us pretend lizards don't eat insects, spiders don't catch flies, tigers love small children. We don't need experts. Tate Britain went through a period when they didn't like labels: in 2013 a curator explained

226. Huang Yong Ping *Vomit Bag* 2017.
227. https://www.artnews.com/art-news/news/depictions-of-animal-cruelty-are-not-art-chinese-con-temporary-art-survey-at-guggenheim-museum-faces-pushback-from-animal-rights-groups-9042/ accessed 6 June 2020.
228. The *New York Times* 13 March 2018.

the policy – "Your response is as valid as our knowledge, and this rehang presents a sort of release for the artist and their work from this encumbrance of academic protocols." (In this case, why have curators? the concept of equating specialist artistic knowledge with guesses from the public standing in front of conceptual art is counter-intuitive). In 2017, it was announced that Tate Britain was going to bring back picture labels to help the public better understand the art."[229] But then what do labels mean? Does wildlife need labels? When we view a beautiful flower do we have to know its name? More importantly, does its name label bring additional value to our experience? I think it does – but it has to be informed by historical and geographical reality, not by a junk label.

The labels on animals may change as they cross the national borders. The migrant Painted Lady becomes *La Belle Dame* as it crosses the Channel, a Scarce Swallowtail becomes the *Flambé*. The Sandhill Rustic becomes *Lupérine de la fétuque* in France (Lepertel & Quinette 2106), *Travařka Nickerlova* in the Czech Republic and *Nickerls Graswurzeleule* in Germany.[230] In Cornwall, there are Cornish names for moths: thus Ruby Tiger is *Tyger Ruby*; the Drinker is *Sughaner*; the Flame Shoulder is *Scoth Flam* (the adjective always follows the noun); the Large Yellow Underwing is *Ys-askel Melen Mur an vrassa*; the Snout is *Tronek* (Spalding & Jenkin 1988). These names bring something of the place to the moth or butterfly.

There is a perception that, since all experiences of meaning in art are self-generated, all experiences are equally valid. In an exhibition by Marlie Mul at Glasgow's Gallery of Modern Art called "This Exhibition Has Been Cancelled", the artist decided to cancel it because none of her proposals could be realised in this space.[231] Instead the gallery was left empty except for large posters proclaiming that the exhibition is cancelled. The curator of contemporary art stated: "removing the exhibition from the gallery space forces us to question the value and function of cultural institutions such as Gallery of Modern Art in contemporary society today. … Perhaps (the) Gallery of Modern Art and, by extension, other museums and galleries would be better placed as a space for another kind of activity?"[232]

In this vacuum the label may become more important, and may increase the importance of the art. This forms the basis of the success of Damian Hirst; who would remember his 1991 dead shark in formaldehyde without the title: *The physical impossibility of death in the mind of someone living*? In an interesting exercise – which at first I thought was an April Fool's joke – Turpin *et al.* (2019) showed that the domain of abstract art perfectly exemplifies an environment in which bullshit labels are both rampant and effective in enhancing the perceived quality of the art. They showed that bullshit can be used effectively as a low-cost

229. The *Daily Telegraph* 26 May 2017.
230. https://lepidoptera.eu/species/1114 accessed 8 June 2020.
231. https://www.studiointernational.com/index.php/marlie-mul-nothing-was-possible-this-exhibition-is-cancelled-glasgow-gallery-of-modern-art accessed 10 June 2020.
232. *Daily Telegraph* 25 May 2017.

strategy to impress others and gain prestige in domains such as abstract art where it is difficult to make objective judgements such as on skill and the achievement of aims. In particular, they showed (using both computer-generated and artist-created paintings) that abstract art accompanied by pseudo-profound bullshit titles (such as *Evolving Model of Dreams*) will be judged as more profound than abstract art either without a title or a mundane title (such as *Objects in Tint*). Randomly generated titles were very effective. The perceived importance of a work of art could also be increased by the use of International Art English – the language used by many artists and artistic scholars to discuss art (Rule & Levine 2012). Its key features include converting verbs and adjectives into nouns (such as *potential* to *potentiality*), the pairing of like terms (such as *internal psychology* and *external reality*) and hard-to-picture spatial metaphors (such as *culmination of many small acts achieves mythic proportions*). This language, used across the world in art circles, hardly resembles correct English – it has "everything to do with English, but is emphatically not English. It is oddly pornographic: we know it when we see it." So the dead Tiger Shark becomes a valuable work of art – at $12,000,000 – but it is still just a dead shark, out of context and a meaningless use of an animal. How much more it should be worth as a live animal in its fiery splendour swimming menacingly around the Pacific islands.

Monogram 1955–1959 is a mix of oil, paper, fabric, printed reproductions, metal, wood, rubber shoe-heel and tennis ball on two conjoined canvases with oil on a taxidermied Angora Goat with a brass plaque and a rubber tyre on a wood platform mounted on four casters. The artist Robert Rauschenberg often worked with stuffed animals with the aim he said "to continue their life, because I always thought, it's too bad they're dead, and so I thought I can do something about that." He saw this goat in a second-hand office supply place. "It looked too much like itself that I couldn't compete with my painting … (and) … refused to be abstracted into art. It looked like art with a goat. And so I put the tire there and then everything went to rest, and they lived happily ever after."[233] This startling work, needing no fancy labels, has been interpreted in many ways, including (unsurprisingly) homoerotic themes, but to Catherine Craft[234] there is a strangely poignant beauty to the acquiescent, eternally patient goat. To me, it says that a goat is a goat even in the weirdest most unnatural artificial situation, the goat dominates its surroundings (in contrast to Hirst's captured, dead meaningless surrounded shark) and emphasises the solid reality of the goat as the focal point of the exhibition.[235]

In contrast, Joan Miró's 1936 81 × 30.1 cm *Objet poétique*, which consists of a stuffed parrot on a wood perch, stuffed silk stocking with velvet garter and doll's

233. Programme notes, Tate Modern 2016.
234. https://uk.phaidon.com/agenda/art/articles/2016/december/06/the-meanings-in-robert-rauschen-berg-s-monogram/ accessed 8 June 2020.
235. Rauschenberg went further. His 1953 work *Erased de Kooning Drawing* is an almost blank piece of paper in a simple gilded frame, the result of rubbing out a drawing he asked Willem de Kooning to produce. Without the inscription, we would have no idea what is in the frame; the piece would be indecipherable. His 1961 work *This Is a Portrait of Iris Clert If I Say So* is a simple telegram with envelope stating this fact – he had forgotten to make a portrait he had promised for an exhibition in Paris.

paper shoe suspended in a hollow wood frame, derby hat, hanging cork ball, celluloid fish, and engraved map, liberates wildlife from their natural context and re-combines them – alienating them from their history. It probably doesn't matter that the original map and fish have been replaced. Rauschenberg used real animals as part of his *Scatole Personali* (1952–53), a series of wood or metal boxes containing found objects and materials, such as beads, dirt, engravings, pebbles and sticks, made during his travels in Italy and North Africa; the keen naturalist notices the lidded painted wood box with a twig and a beetle and a box with a twig with a winged insect on an engraving.

The painting *Olive Trees* by Van Gogh contains the remains of a grasshopper (minus its abdomen and thorax) embedded in the paint in the lower foreground of the landscape.[236] Van Gogh worked outside directly from nature amongst the dust, grass, flies and grasshoppers.[237] There was no sign of struggling in the surrounding paint, indicating that the grasshopper was either dead before landing on the canvas or died immediately afterwards; perhaps Van Gogh killed it with the end of the brush as it landed. We can guess that the painting was painted in plein-air in the late summer when the grasshopper had fully developed. The addition of the grasshopper adds a dimension and context to the painting.

Animals can get their own back. Congo the chimpanzee was a famous artist. He prolifically churned out abstract art for three years in the late 1950s sitting in a chair in front of a table with paper and paint, producing over 400 works during a research study by Desmond Morris who said of Congo "No other apes were controlling the mark making and varying the patterns as he was."[238] Congo had his own show in London in December 2019 – although too late for him to see it as he died in 1964. He was considered to be the Picasso of the simian world. Morris claimed that "Congo's ability to make a controlled abstract pattern and then to vary it in different ways meant that inside the ape brain there was already an aesthetic sense – very primitive but nevertheless present in a non-human species. … Watching him paint was like witnessing the birth of art." Some of his paintings are very striking, if rather abstract. His bold painting *Split-Fan Pattern with Central Black Spot* (1957), with black, yellow and blue movements over a red background, strikingly reminds me of Roger Hilton gouache paintings produced whilst on his alcoholic death bed in the early 1970s in a tiny cottage near St Just.

People can pretend to be animals of course. In a bizarre experiment in 2000, Jan Fabre (great grandson of the famous 19th century naturalist Jean-Henri Fabre) filmed normally staid staff at the Natural History Museum jumping about dressed as butterflies and beetles, including the then Keeper of the Department of

236. *Daily Telegraph* 9 November 2017.
237. "just go and sit outdoors, painting on the spot itself! Then all sorts of things like the following happen – I must have picked up a good hundred flies and more off the 4 canvases that you'll [his brother Theo] be getting …" https://nelson-atkins.org/grasshopper-found-embedded-van-gogh-masterpiece/ accessed 10 June 2020.
238. https://news.artnet.com/exhibitions/congo-late-chimpanzee-painter-whose-work-sold-thousands-will-solo-show-december-1671976 accessed 6 December 2019.

Entomology, Dick Vane-Wright, as a giant butterfly; extracts from the film can be seen at https://vimeo.com/132641935. Fabre explained his work *A Consilience* in this way: "I want to explore new interpretations for art and science with this piece, where the borders of these two disciplines touch each other ... I wanted to learn from the entomologists – perhaps change the way they look at things. ... Consilience is literally a 'jumping together' of knowledge and facts across disciplines to create a common groundwork of explanation, as reflected in my approach to the Museum and its science." It was certainly fun for the participants, but to me showed the huge gulf there is between giant men dressed in unrealistic costumes and masks jumping around in ungainly fashion and the minute intricate world of delicate insects. For the participants, it must have been a huge change from staring through microscopes at pinned insects or the endless shuffling round of museum specimens that normally occupy their days.

A painting by Van Gogh is worth huge sums unless it is shown to be a forgery and then it becomes almost worthless. Superficially it is the same painting, but it lacks authenticity, it lacks provenance, it lacks historical connection – it is out of place and out of its time. In original paintings "one follows the traces of the painter's immediate gestures. In this special sense all [original] paintings are contemporary" (Berger 1972).

What price reality? The Chauvet Cave in the Ardèche region of southern France, discovered as recently as 1994, contains cave art paintings dated to between 30,000 and 33,000 years ago including the *Megaloceros* (an extinct type of giant moose) drawn in charcoal, cave bears painted in red, a long-eared Owl (engraved onto the rock) looking back over it body, two lions (male and female) in black, seven bison pursued by a pride of sixteen lions in black, a panther[239], mammoths, a musk ox (all in black) and even a half human and half bison creature. The cave was sealed off as soon as it was discovered to prevent damage unwittingly caused by the thousands of expected visitors – damage from light, increases in temperature and humidity, increases in carbon dioxide. Nearby was built a huge concrete hanger to hold an imitation Chauvet Cave, with walls of concrete instead of limestone, stalagmites and stalactites made of resin and cave paintings on the walls. "It's hoped that the replica will bring these ancient artists closer still, as their testimony to human culture and creativity opens to the crowds ... Or, at least, a copy of that testimony."[240] But can it be the same? It is more real than a digital experience on your computer, but worse than the original. Is it art? There can be no awe at the creativity of our ancestors, no sense of history, mystery, darkness, no sense that mammoths walked outside these caves whilst man painted within, no sense that these paintings survived in order that we might see them after 30,000 years. Worse than that – does the replica reduce the original, make it less real and less important? The animal paintings, however accurately redrawn, using digital images projected onto the canvases, are fake, out of time, with no real connection to our past and

---

239. To me, one of the animal representations looks rather like a hyena.
240. https://www.bbc.co.uk/news/science-environment-32403867

as such become just more images; these animals existed in the imagination of the people at the time as real objects, in some cases terrifying predators, and they are reduced now as copied images on a fake wall.

There is a close link between animals and painting – "probably the first paint was animal blood" (Berger 2009) – but there are different ways of seeing our wildlife, and indeed the objects around us. We need to look beyond external appearance and look for the internal quality of things. These things are more than just their external appearance. In the classic phrase from Heidegger (1927) "a table is not just a table" in a void, it may be a family table, a place where a decision was made, a place where work was written. A glass of milk is a glass of milk – but in each glass the milk may differ in colour and quality; for example, the milk from cows feeding on grass outdoors has better nutritional profile of proteins, fatty acids and antioxidants than milk from cows reared indoors and fed intensively.[241] A cup of coffee mixed with that milk could be defined in terms of its chemistry, the botany of the coffee plant, how it is made, the effect of caffeine on the body, the international coffee trade or, alternatively, defined in our personal sentimental associations from its rich aroma, warmth, smell and colour, and even the sensations anticipated when we make or buy it.[242] Each object, each animal, each plant, has more about it than mere physical appearance. "Even the slightest thing contains a little that is unknown. We must find it. To describe a blazing fire or a tree in a plain, we must remain before that fire or that tree until they no longer resemble for us any other tree or any other fire."[243] Individual animals and plants, even objects, change with time; a lamb becomes a sheep, a caterpillar becomes a moth. Living things die and decompose or become fossilised. The Scot John Muir (quoted in Wulf 2015) said: "A dead pine, is no more a pine than a dead human carcass is a man – no doubt these trees would make good lumber after passing through a sawmill, as George Washington after passing through the hands of a French cook would have made good food." We need to define in our terms what we see, and note the individuality of each animal and each plant. This is where Hirst's dead shark fails, as it has no history, no individuality.

The same object may be seen in different ways. If you visit a nudist beach you will see lots of naked people, women and men, naked rather nude[244]; there is a difference between nudity and nakedness. To be naked is to be oneself, to reveal oneself, to be without disguise (Berger 1972). To be nude is to be seen naked by others and yet not recognised for oneself; to be nude is to be on display; in a way therefore nudity is a form of dress. A naked body has to be seen as an object in order to become a nude. So unclothed people on the beach might be naked

---

241. *New Scientist* 3043 11/10/2015; pp 33–37.
242. This is Husserl phenomenology, where in phenomenological reduction we strip away any theorising about what coffee really is until we are left only with the intense and immediate flavour – the phenomenon.
243. Gustave Flaubert writing to Guy de Maupassant in 1870.
244. If you called it a naked beach it would imply that the beach was without clothes, i.e. without a covering of sand or shingle.

– without any disguise – or nude – on display as an object, perhaps of desire. The beautiful statue by Antonio Canova of the Three Graces, daughters of Zeus, shows naked women, unaware of being viewed – although to the viewer they may be seen to be nude, objects of desire. This we bring our own perceptions to the object.

An ordinary object may be designated as art and displayed as a way of getting the observer to look again and re-assess their view. Thus is Duchamp's *Urinal* (1917), since lost and replaced in the Tate Gallery by a 1964 replica (rather like Trigger's broom in the BBC sitcom *Only Fools and Horses* – he had the same broom for 20 years but in that time it had 17 new heads and 14 new handles).[245] Duchamp took an ordinary article of life, called it *Fountain* and placed it so that its significance and meaning changed, creating a new thought for that object. In classic art language, looking for connections and interpretation, we read on the Tate's website[246] that "The intimate nature of the function of the urinal, and its highly gendered character, also resonated strongly with the complex psycho-physical themes of the masterpiece he was working on at the time, *The Bride Stripped Bare by her Bachelors, Even 1915–23*."[247] The fact that the urinal on display is an approximate replica is not thought relevant by the Tate's management. Although in many ways a fake, it makes us look at things in a different way in the context of our own imaginings.

The artist David Measures turned his back on modern art. "Few pursuits could be further from the sinking pit of Conceptualism than painting butterflies in watercolour in the wild" (Spalding, J. 2016). Painting was for him "a way of capturing not only the essence of a living creature but also his excitement at seeing it" (Spalding, J. 2016). His butterflies were living, not dead on a pin, spontaneous, finished in the wild where he stood painting with his fingertips and nails, enriched by spit, and enhanced by coloured notes of behaviour; they were about the butterflies and our awareness of them, about brief life not death, each illustrated as an individual not as a uniform representation of the species as an illustration in a text book.

So we look again, and more closely, at animals and plants in the context of their individuality, their history and geography. Animals are more than their physical form. They exist within their historical setting, within their habitat, within their past and their evolutionary future, outside and beyond man, and within man and his circle, within their movements (self-propelled and involuntary) and we bring to our view of them the weight of our understanding.

---

245. The *Urinal* you can see in many modern art galleries around the world are not originals by Duchamp but one of the many replicas he had made in the 1960s. Even more confusingly, several scholars have now argued that the original *Urinal* was not Duchamp's at all but a remarkable feminist anti-war gesture by the brilliant Dada poet, Baroness Elsa von Freytag-Loringhoven.
246. https://www.tate.org.uk/art/artworks/duchamp-fountain-t07573 accessed 11 June 2020.
247. Even this was reconstructed in 1965–6 and the lower panel remade in 1985.

REFERENCES

Agassiz, D. 2017. The mystery of *Euzophera costivittella* Ragonot, 1887 (Lepidoptera: Pyralidae) in Britain. *Entomologist's Gazette*. **68**: 57–59.

Agassiz, D.J.L., Beavan, S.D. & Heckford, R.J. 2013. *Checklist of the Lepidoptera of the British Isles. Handbooks for Identification of British Insects.* Royal Entomological Society.

Agassiz, D.J.L., Beavan, S.D. & Heckford, R.J. 2015. Dataset: Checklist of the Lepidoptera of the British Isles – Data. Resource: Checklist of the Lepidoptera of the British Isles [Agassiz, Beavan & Heckford] (amended 19/2/2016). Natural History Museum Data Portal (data.nhm.ac.uk). https://doi.org/10.5519/0093915 Retrieved: 16:46 20 Apr 2020 (GMT).

Alerstam, A., Chapman, J.W., Bäckman, J., Smith, A.D., Karlsson, H., Nilsson, C., Reynolds, D.R., Klaassen, R.H.G. & Hill, J.K. 2011. Convergent patterns of long-distance nocturnal migration in noctuid moths and passerine birds. *Proceedings of the Royal Society B.* **278**: 3074–3080.

Alexander, K., Green, T. & Morris, R. 2016. Naturalised broadleaf trees – a call for a strategic reappraisal. *British Wildlife*. **28**: 13–20.

Alexander, K.N.A. 2008. *The land and freshwater bugs (Hemiptera) of Cornwall and the Isles of Scilly*. CISFBR & ERCCIS Occasional Publication No 2. Camborne.

Al-Khalili, J. & McFadden, J. 2014. *Life on the Edge: The Coming of Age of Quantum Biology*. Black Swan. London.

Allan, P.B.M. 1948. *Moths and Memories*. Watkins & Doncaster. London.

Altermatt, F. & Ebert, D. 2016. Reduced flight-to-light behaviour of moth populations exposed to long-term urban light pollution. *Biology Letters*. **12**: 20160111.

Anonymous. 1882. *The Journal of Science, and Annals of Astronomy, Biology, geology, Industrial Architecture, Manufactures and Technology*. **4**: 208.

Asher, J., Warren, M., Fox, R., Harding, P., Jeffcoate, G. & Jeffcoate, S. 2001. *The Millennium Atlas of Butterflies in Britain and Ireland*. Oxford University Press. Oxford.

Atkinson, T.C., Briffa, K.R. & Coope, G.R. 1987. Seasonal temperatures in Britain during the past 22,000 years, reconstructed using beetle remains. *Nature*. **325**: 587–592.

Baker, R.R & Sadovy, Y. 1978. The distance and nature of the light trap response of moths. *Nature*. **276:** 818–821.

Bakewell, S. 2016. *At the Existentialist Café. Freedom, Being and Apricot Cocktails*. Chatto & Windus. London.

Barreto, G.R., Rushton, S.P., Strachan, R. & Macdonald, D.W. 1998. The role of habitat and mink predation in determining the status and distribution of water voles in England. *Animal Conservation forum*. 1(2): 129–137.

Bartlett, J.C., Convey, P., Pertierra, L.R. & Hayward, S.A.L. 2020. An insect invasion of Antarctica:the past, present and future distribution of *Eretmoptera murphyi* (Diptera, Chironomidae) on Signy Island. *Insect Conservation & Diversity*. **13**: 77–90.

Beatty, G.E. & Provan, J. 2013. Post-glacial dispersal, rather than in in situ glacial survival, best explains the disjunct distribution of the Lusitanian plant species *Daboecia cantabrica* (Ericaceae). *Journal of Biogeography*. **40**: 335–344.

Beebee, T. 2014. Ireland's Lusitanian wildlife: unravelling a mystery. *British Wildlife*. **25**: 229–235.

Beebee, T.J.C., Buckley, J., Evans, I., Foster, J.P., Gent, A.H., Gleed-Owen, C.P., Kelly, G., Rowe, G., Snell, C., Wycherley, J.T. & Zeisset, I. 2005. Neglected native or undesirable alien? Resolution of a conservation dilemma concerning the pool frog *Rana lessonae*. *Biodiversity & Conservation*. **14**: 1607. https://doi.org/10.1007/s10531-004-0532-3

Beirne, B.P. 1947. *The Origin and History of the British fauna*. Methuen & Co. London.

Bere, R. 1982. *The Nature of Cornwall*. Barracuda Books. Buckingham.

Berger, J. 1972. *Ways of Seeing*. Penguin Books. London.

Berger, J. 2009. *Why Look at Animals*. Penguin Books. London.

Bhagwat, S.A. & Willis, K.J. 2008. Species persistence in northerly glacial refugia of Europe: a matter of chance or biogeographical traits? *Journal of Biogeography*. **35**: 464–482.

Bilton, D. 1994. Phylogeography and recent historical biogeography of *Hydroporus glabriusculus* Aubé (Coleoptera: Dytiscidae) in the British Isles and Scandinavia. *Biological Journal of the Linnean Society*. **51**: 293–307.

Birkenshaw, N. & Thomas, C.D. 1999. Torch-light transect surveys for moths. *Journal of Insect Conservation*. **3**: 15–24.

Birks, H.J.B. & Willis, K.J. 2008. Alpines, trees, and refugia in Europe. *Plant Ecology & Diversity*. **1**(2): 147–160.

Blunt, A.G., Shaw, A.S. & Shaw, J.F. 2017. Small Nettle *Urtica urens* L. a hostplant for Lepidoptera in Shropshire. *British Journal of Entomology and Natural History*. **30**: 225–236.

Bradley, J.D. & Fletcher, D.S. 1979. *A Recorder's Log Book or Label List of British Butterflies and Moths*. Natural History Museum. London.

Bradshaw, A.D. & Chadwick, M.J. 1980. *The Restoration of Land. The ecology and reclamation of derelict and degraded land*. Blackwell Scientific Publications. Oxford.

Brattström, O., Bensch, S., Wassenaar, L.I., Hobson, K.A. & Åkesson, S. 2010. Understanding the migration ecology of European red admirals *Vanessa atalanta* using stable hydrogen isotopes. *Ecography*. **33**: 720–729.

Brattström, O., Kjellén, N., Alerstam, T. & Åkesson, S. 2008. Effects of wind and weather on red admiral, *Vanessa atalanta*, migration at a coastal site in southern Sweden. *Animal Behaviour*. **76**: 335–344.

British Museum (Natural History) Economic Series No. 14. *Clothes moths and House Moths*. London.

Brown, P.M.J. & Roy, H.E. 2018. Native ladybird decline caused by the invasive harlequin *Harmonia axyridis*: evidence from a long-term field study. *Insect Conservation & Diversity*. **11**: 230–239.

Bryce, R., Oliver, M.K., Davies, L., Gray, H., Urquhart, J. & Lambin, X. 2011.

Turning back the tide of American mink invasion at an unprecedented scale through community participation and adaptive management. *Biological Conservation*. **144**(1). 575–583.

Calosi, P., Bilton, D., Spicer, J. & Atfield, A. 2008. Thermal tolerance and geographical range size in the *Agabus brunneus* group of European diving beetles (Coleoptera: Dytiscidae). *Journal of Biogeography*. **35**: 295–305. 10.1111/j.1365-2699.2007.01787.x.

Cameron, D. 2019. *For the Record*. William Collins. London.

Carthey, A.J.R. & Banks, P.B. 2012. When Does an Alien Become a Native Species? A Vulnerable Native Mammal Recognizes and Responds to Its Long-Term Alien Predator. *PLOS One*. DOI: 10.1371/journal.pone.0031804.

Chapman, J.W., Drake, V.A. & Reynolds, D.R. 2011. Recent insights from radar studies of insect flight. *Annual Review of Entomology*. **56**: 337–356.

Chapman, J.W., Lim, K.S. & Reynolds, D.R. 2013. The significance of midsummer movements of *Autographa gamma*: Implications for a mechanistic understanding of orientation behavior in a migrant moth. *Current Zoology*. **59**(3): 360–370.

Chapman, J.W., Nesbit, R.L., Burgin, L.E., Reynolds, D.R., Smith, A.D., Middleton, D.R. & Hill, J.K. 2010. Flight orientation behaviours promote optimal migration trajectories in high-flying insects. *Science*. **327**: 682–685.

Chapman J.W., Reynolds, D.R., Mouritsen, H., J Hill, J.K., Riley, J.R., Sivell, D., Smith, A.D. & Woiwod, I.P. 2008. Wind selection and drift compensation optimize migratory pathways in a high-flying moth. *Current Biology*. https://doi.org/10.1016/j.cub.2008.02.080.

Cinzano, P., Falchi, F. & Elvidge, C.D. 2001.The first World Atlas of the artificial night sky brightness. *Monthly Notices of the Royal Astronomical Society*. **328**: 689–707.

Coe, J. 2015. *Number 11*. Penguin Books. UK.

Combe, F.J., Ellis, J.S., Lloyd, K.L., Cain, B., Wheater, C.P. & Harris, W.E. 2016. After the Ice Age: The impact of post-glacial dispersal on the phylogeography of a small mammal, *Muscardinus avellanarius*. *Frontiers in Ecology and Evolution*. **4**: Article 72. doi: 10.3389/fevo.2016.00072.

Cook, G.A. 2007. Botanical Exchanges: Jean-Jacques Rousseau and the Duchess of Portland. *History of European Ideas*. **33**(2): 142–156.

Cook, L. & McConville, C. 2018. Lord Walsingham and the Manchester Moth. *Entomologist's Gazette*. **69**: 47–63.

Cooper. J.F. 1826. *The Last of the Mohicans*. W.A. Townsend & Company. New York.

Cope, G.R. 1997. Fossil coleopteran assemblages as sensitive indicators of climatic changes during the Devensian (Last) cold stage. *Royal Society B*. **280**: 313–340.

Corbet, P.S. 2000. the first recorded arrival of *Anax junius*, Drury (Anisoptera: Aeshnidae) in Europe: A scientist's perspective. *International Journal of Odonatology*. **3**(2): 153–162. DOI: 10.1080/13887890.2000.9748146.

Cranston, P.S. 2016. Madagascan "wild" silk. *Antenna*. **40**:114–118.

Dacke, M., Baird, E., Byrne, M., Scholtz, C.H. & Warrant, E.J. 2013. Dung Beetles use the Milky Way for orientation. *Current Biology*. **23**: 298–300. http://dx.doi.

org/10.1016/j.cub.2012.12.034.

Dacke, M., Nilsson, D.-E., Scholtz, C.H., Marcus Byrne, M. & Warrant, E.J. 2003. Animal behaviour: Insect orientation to polarized moonlight. *Nature*. **424**: 33 doi:10.1038/424033a.

Danthanarayana, W. 1976. Environmentally cued size variation in the light-brown apple moth, *Epiphyas postvittana* (Walk.) (Tortricidae), and its adaptive value in dispersal. *Oecologia*. **26**: 121–132

Dapporto, L., Habel, J.C., Dennis, R.L.H. & Schmitt, T. 2011. The biogeography of the western Mediterranean: elucidating contradictory distribution patterns of differentiation in *Maniola jurtina* (Lepidoptera: Nymphalidae). *Biological Journal of the Linnean Society*. **103**: 571–577.

Davey, P. 2006. Pattons' Tiger *Hyphoraia testudinaria* – Adventive or Immigrant? *Atropos*. **28**: 81.

de Beaulieu, F. 2005. *Quand on parle du loup en Bretagne*. Éditions Le Télégramme.

De Cock, R. 2009. Biology and behaviour of European lampyrids. In: V.B. Meyer-Rochow (ed.), *Bioluminescence in focus—a collection of illuminating essays* (pp. 161–200). Research Signpost. Kerala, India.

Dennis, R.L.H. 1992. An evolutionary history of British butterflies. In: R.L.H. Dennis. (ed.) *The Ecology of Butterflies in Britain*. Oxford University Press. Oxford.

Dennis, R.L.H. 1993. *Butterflies and Climate Change*. Manchester University Press. Manchester.

Dennis, R.L.H. & Schmitt, T. 2009. Faunal structures, paleography and historical inference. In: Settele, J., van Dyck, H., Konvicka, M. & Shreeve, T.G. (eds.) *Ecology of Butterflies in Europe*. Cambridge University Press. Cambridge.

Didham, R.K., Leather, S.R. & Basset, Y. 2016. Circle the bandwagons – challenges mount against the theoretical foundations of applied functional trait and ecosystem service research. *Insect Conservation and Diversity*. **9**: 1–3.

Dines, T. 2016. Keeping the wild in wildflower. *British Wildlife*. **28**: 112–117.

Dingle, H. & Drake, V.A. 2007. What is Migration? *BioScience*. **57**(2): 113–121.

Doak, D.F., Bakker, V.J., Goldstein, B.E. & Hale, B. 2014. What is the future of conservation? *Trends in Ecology & Evolution*. **29**: 77–81. doi: 10.1016/ j.tree.2013.10.013.

Dockx, C. 2007. Directional and stabilizing selection on wing size and shape in migrant and resident monarch butterflies, *Danaus plexippus* (L.), in Cuba. *Biological Journal of the Linnean Society*. **92**: 605–616.

Dodson, C.A., Hore, P.J. & Wallace, M.I. 2013. A radical sense of direction: signalling and mechanism in cryptochrome magnetoreception. *Trends in biochemical sciences*. **38**(9): 435–446.

DOE (Minerals Division). 1994. *The Reclamation and Management of Metalliferous Mining Sites*. Environmental Consultancy (University of Sheffield) and Richards Moorehead & Lang Ltd. HMSO. London.

Dorhout, D.L., Sappington, T.W. & Rice, M.E. 2008. Evidence for obligate migratory flight behavior in young European corn borer (Lepidoptera: Crambidae) females. *Environmental Entomology*. **37**: 1280–1290.

Dover, J.W. 1991. The conservation of insects on arable farmland. In: N.M. Collins & J.A. Thomas (eds). *The Conservation of Insects and their Habitats. 15th Symposium of the Royal Entomological Society of London.* Academic Press. London.

Doyle, G.J. 1990. The history of *Erica erigena* R. Ross, an Irish plant with a disjunct European distribution. *Journal of Quaternary Science.* **5**: 1–16.

Dreisig, H. 1975. Environmental control of the daily onset of luminescent activity in glowworms and fireflies (Coleoptera: Lampyridae). *Oecologia.* **18**: 85–99. https://doi.org/10.1007/BF00348090.

Dunham, K., Ghiurghi, A., Cumbi, R. & Urbano, F. 2010. Human–wildlife conflict in Mozambique: a national perspective, with emphasis on wildlife attacks on humans. *Oryx.* **44**(2): 185–193.

Eeles, P. 2019. *Life Cycles of British & Irish Butterflies.* Pisces Publications. Newbury.

Eisenbeis, G. 2006. Artificial night lighting and insects: Attraction of insects to streetlamps in a rural setting in Germany. In: C. Rich & T. Longcore (eds). *Ecological Consequences of Artificial Night Lighting.* Island Press. Washington.

Ellington, C.P., van den Berg, C., Willmott, A.P. & Thomas, A.L.R. 1996. Leading-edge vortices in insect flight. *Nature.* **384**: 626–630.

Emmet, A.M. 1991. Chart showing the life history and habits of the British Lepidoptera. In: A.M. Emmet, A.M. & J. Heath (eds.). *The Moths and Butterflies of Great Britain and Ireland. Volume 7(2).* Harley Books. Essex.

Faillie, L. & Nicolle, M. 2003. Motorways as routes for the expansion of some *Zygaena* species (Lepidoptera: Zygaenidae, Zygaeninae) in west-central France. In: Efetov, K.A., Tremewan, W.G. & Tarmann, G.M. *Proceedings of the 7th International Symposium on Zygaenidae, Innsbruck, 2000.* Crimean State Medical University Press. Simferopol.

Falchi, F., Cinzano, P., Duriscoe, D., Kyba, C. C., Elvidge, C. D., Baugh, K. & Furgoni, R. 2016. The new world atlas of artificial night sky brightness. *Science Advance.* **2**, e1600377.

Falk-Petersen, J. Bøhn, T. & Sandlund, O.T. 2006. On the numerous concepts in Invasion Biology. *Biological Invasions.* **8**: 1409–1424. DOI: 10.1007/s10530-005-0710-6

Farjon, A. 2015. How old can a tree be? A rebuttal of claims of extraordinary ages of trees and other organisms in recent research and popular science literature. *The Linnean.* **31**(2): 23–29.

Fay, T.P, Lindoy, L.P., Manolopoulos, D.E. & Hore, P.J. 2019. How quantum is radical pair magnetoreception? *Faraday Discussions.* https://doi.org/10.1039/C9FD00049F.

Feltwell, J. & Philp, J. 1980. Natural history of the M20 motorway. *Transactions of the Kent Field Club.* **8**(2):101–114.

ffrench-Constant, R.H., Somers-Yeates, R., Bennie, J., Economou, T., Hodgson, D., Spalding, A. & McGregor, P.K. 2016. Light pollution is associated with earlier tree budburst across the United Kingdom. *Proceedings of the Royal Society B.* **283**: 20160813.

Fischer, B & Larson, B.M.H. 2019. Collecting insects to conserve them: a call for ethical caution. *Insect Conservation and Diversity*. **12**: 173–182.

Ford, E.B. 1972. *Moths*. The New Naturalist. 3rd Edition. Collins. London.

Fox, R., Parsons, M.S., Chapman, J.W., Woiwod, I.P., Warren, M.S. & Brooks, D.R. 2013. *The State of Britain's Larger Moths 2013*. Butterfly Conservation and Rothamsted Research, Wareham, Dorset, UK.

French, C.N. 2020. *A Flora of Cornwall*. Wheal Seton Press. Camborne.

French, C.N., Murphy, R.J. & Atkinson, M.G.C. 1999. *Flora of Cornwall*. Wheal Seton Press. Camborne.

Fric Z., Klímová M., Konvička M. 2006. Mechanical design indicates mobility differences among butterfly generations. *Evolutionary Ecology Research*. **8**: 1511–1522.

Fry, R. & Lonsdale, D. 1991. *Habitat Conservation for Insects – A Neglected Green Issue*. AES. Middlesex.

Gaston, K.J. 2018. Lighting up the nighttime. Artificial light at night needs to be reduced to limit negative environmental impacts. *Science*. **362** (6416): 744–746.

Gatehouse A.G. 1997. Behaviour and ecological genetics of wind-borne migration by insects. 1997. *Annual Review of Entomology*. **42**: 475–502.

Graham, W. 1946. *Demelza*. Collins. London.

Graham, W. 1963. *The Grove of Eagles*. Fontana. London.

Gregory, S.J. 2016. On the terrestrial Landhopper *Arcitalitrus dorrieni* (Hunt, 1925) (Amphipoda: Talitridae): identification and current distribution. *Bulletin of the British Myriapod & Isopod Group*. **29**:1–13.

Griffiths, J. 2008. *Wild: An Elemental Journey*. Penguin Books. London.

Guagnin, M., Shipton, C., el-Dossary, S., al-Rashid, M., Moussa, F., Stewart, M., Ott, F., Alsharekh, A. & Petraglia, M.D. 2018. Rock art provides new evidence on the biogeography of kudu (*Tragelaphus imberbis*), wild dromedary, aurochs (*Bos primigenius*) and African wild ass (*Equus africanus*) in the early and middle Holocene of north-western Arabia. *Journal of Biogeography*. 1–14. https://doi.org/10.1111/jbi.13165.

Guerra, P.A., Gegear, R.J. & Reppert, S.M. 2014. A magnetic compass aids monarch butterfly migration. *Nature communications*. **5**:1–8.

Gunn, P. & Gunn, B. 2012. Lunar effects on the bioluminescent activity of the glow-worm *Lampyris noctiluca* and its larvae. *Lampyrid*. **3**: 1–16.

Hamdorf, K. & Högland, G. 1981. Light induced retinal screening pigment migration independent of visual cell activity. *Journal of Comparative Physiology*. **143**: 305–309.

Hancock, E.G. 2018. Netted Carpet *Eustroma reticulata* (D. & S., 1775), (Lep.: Geometridae) as a commodity. *Entomologist's Record and Journal of Variation*. **130**: 123–138.

Harberd, D.J. 1961. Observations on population structure and longevity of Red Fescue L. *New Phytologist*. **61**: 184–210.

Harding, P.T. & Sutton, S.L. 1988. The spread of the terrestrial amphipod *Arcitalitrus dorrieni* in Britain and Ireland: watch this niche! *Isopoda*. **2**: 7–10.

Hardy, P.B., Jeffcoate, G.E. & Dennis, R.L.D. 2017. Butterflies (Papilionoidea) on the Isle of Man: losses, gains and predictions. *Entomologist's Gazette*. **68**: 239–254.

Harris, M. 1775. *The English Lepidoptera; Or, the Aurelian's Pocket Companion*. Printed for J. Robson. London.

Harris, S. & Yalden, D.W. (Eds.) 2008. *Mammals of the British Isles: handbook, 4th Edition*. The Mammal Society. Southampton.

Harrison, T. 1984. *The World Within. A Borneo Story*. Oxford University Press. Oxford.

Hart Dyke, Z. 1949. *So spins the silkworm*. Rockliff. London.

Heckford, R.J. & Beavan, S.D. 2020. Discovery in Cornwall, England of the larva of the Tasmanian species *Barea asbolaea* (Meyrick, 1883) (Lepidoptera: Oecophoridae), together with an account of all the early stages. *Entomologist's Gazette*. **71**: 75–92.

Heidegger, M. 1927. *Sein und Zeit*. Max Niemeyer Verlag. Tübingen.

Henwood, B., Spalding, A. & McCormick, R. 2004. A previously unrecorded foodplant for *Lygephila craccae* ([Denis & Schiffermüller], 1775) (Lepidoptera: Noctuidae) in Great Britain. *Entomologist's Gazette*. **55**: 91–92.

Herzog, H. 2011. *Some we love, some we hate, some we eat. Why it's hard to think straight about animals*. Harper Perennial. New York.

Hewitt, G.M. 1999. Post-glacial recolonisation of European biota. *Biological Journal of the Linnean Society*. **68**: 87–112.

Hill, J.K., Thomas, C.D. & Lewis, O.T. 1999. Flight morphology in fragmented populations of a rare British butterfly, *Hesperia comma. Biological Conservation*. **87**: 277–283.

Hobbs, R.J., Arico, S., Aronson, J., Baron, J.S., Bridgewater, P., Cramer, V.A., Epstein, P.R., Ewel, J.J., Klink, C.A., Lugo, A.E., Norton, D., Ojima, D., Richardson, D.M., Sanderson, E.W., Valladares, F., Vila, M., Zamora, R. & Zobel, M. 2006. Novel ecosystems: theoretical and management aspects of the new ecological world order. *Global Ecology and Biogeography*. **15**: 1–7. doi: 10.1111/j.1466-822x.2006.00212.x.

Hobson, K.A., Doward, K., Kardynal, K.J. & McNeil, J.N. 2018. Inferring origins of migrating insects using isoscapes: a case study using the true armyworm, *Mythimna unipuncta*, in North America. *Ecological Entomology*. **43**: 332–341.

Hof, A., Campagne, P., Rigden, D.J., Yung, C.J., Lingley, J., Quail, M.A., Hall, N., Darby, A.C. & Saccheri, I.J. 2016. The industrial melanism mutation in British peppered moths is a transposable element. *Nature*. **534**: 102–105. https://doi.org/10.1038/nature17951.

Hofmann, A.F. & Tremewan, W.G. 2017. *The Natural History of Burnet Moths. Part 1*. Museum Witt Munich & Nature Research Center. Vilnius.

Hölker, F., Wolter, C., Perkin, E.K. & Tockner, K. 2010. Light pollution as a biodiversity threat. *Trends in Ecology & Evolution*. **25**: 681–682.

Holyoak, D.T. 2009. Bryophytes: Liverworts, Hornworts and Mosses. In: CISBR. *Red Data Book for Cornwall and the Isles of Scilly*. 2nd Edition. Croceago Press. Praze-an-Beeble.

Hopkin, S.P. & Hames, C.A.C. 1994. Zinc, among a 'cocktail' of metal pollutants, is responsible for the absence of the terrestrial isopod *Porcellio scaber* from the vicinity of a primary smelting works. *Ecotoxicology*. **3**: 68–78.

Hopkins, J., Baudry, G., Candolin, U., & Kaitala, A. 2015. I'm sexy and I glow it: Female ornamentation in a nocturnal capital breeder. *Biology Letters*. **11**: 20150599. https://doi.org/10.1098/rsbl.2015.0599.

Hsiao, H.S. 1973. Flight paths of night-flying moths to light. *Journal of Insect Physiology*. **19**: 1971–1976.

Hu, G., Lim, K.S., Reynolds D.R., Reynolds, A.M. & Chapman, J.W. 2016. Wind-related orientation patterns in diurnal, crepuscular and nocturnal high-altitude insect migrants. *Frontiers in Behavioral Neuroscience*. doi: 10.3389/fnbeh.2016.00032.

International Atomic Energy Agency. 2006. *Environmental Consequences of the Chernobyl Accident and Their Remediation: Twenty Years of Experience*. Report of The Chernobyl Forum Expert Group 'Environment'. Vienna.

Jaffe, B.J., Ketterer, M.E. & Smith, D.S. 2018. An arsenic hyperaccumulating fern, *Pteris vittata* L. (Pteridaceae) broadly affects terrestrial invertebrate abundance. *Ecological Entomology*. **43**: 76–84.

Jantzen, B. & Eisner, T. 2008. Hindwings are unnecessary for flight but essential for execution of normal evasive flight in Lepidoptera. *Proceedings of the National Academy of Sciences of the United States of America*. **105**: 16636–16640.

Jenkin, L.E.T., Mann, S.L., Pryor, D. & Keen, T. 1996. The effects of metal contamination on the type and distribution of saltmarsh vegetation in Cornish estuaries. In: Merot, P & Jigorel, A (eds.). *Hydrologie dans les pays celtiques*. INRA. Paris.

John, E., Stefanescu, C., Honey, M. R., Crawford, M. & Taylor, D. 2015. Ceremonial releases of *Danaus plexippus* (Linnaeus,1758) (Lepidoptera: Nymphalidae, Danainae) in the Iberian Peninsula, the Balearic Islands and Cyprus: implications for biogeography, potential colonisation and a provisional listing of Asclepiadoideae from these regions. *Entomologist's Gazette*. **66**: 141–156.

Johns, F., Oakes, L., Oakes, H. & Tunmore, M. 2016. The first British record of *Euchromius ramburiellus* (Dup., 1836). *Atropos*. **56**: 26–30.

Jones, R. 2017. *Call of Nature: the Secret Life of Dung*. Pelagic Publishing. Exeter.

Joyce, D.A. & Pullin, A.S. 2001. Phylogeography of the Marsh Fritillary *Euphydryas aurinia* (Lepidoptera: Nymphalidae) in the UK. *Biological Journal of the Linnean Society*. **72**: 129–141. https://doi.org/10.1111/j.1095-8312.2001.tb01305.x.

Joyce, D.A. & Pullin, A.S. 2003. Conservation implications of the distribution of genetic diversity at different scales: a case study using the marsh fritillary butterfly (*Euphydryas aurinia*). *Biological Conservation*. **114**(3): 453–461.

Juniper, T. 2013. *What Has Nature Ever Done for Us*. Profile Books. London.

Kennedy, J.S. 1985. Migration: behaviorial and ecological. In: M.A. Rankin (ed.) Migrations: mechanisms and adaptive significance. *Contributions in Marine Science*. **27**: 5–26.

Kertész, K., Piszter, G., Bálint, Z. & Biró, L.P. 2019. Biogeographical patterns in the structural blue of male *Polyommatus icarus* butterflies. *Scientific Reports*. DOI: 10.1038/s41598-019-38827-w.

King, M. 2017. The Knepp Vera conference: the case for creating new wood pastures. *British Wildlife*. **29**: 27–33.

Kjer, K.M., Simon, C., Yavorskaya, M. & Beutel, R.G. 2016. Progress, pitfalls and parallel universes: a history of insect phylogenetics. *Journal of the Royal Society Interface*. https://doi.org/10.1098/rsif.2016.0363.

Kolbert, E. 2014. *The Sixth Extinction*. Bloomsbury. London.

Kristensen, N.P. & Skalski, A.W. 1998. Phylogeny and palaeontology. In: Kristensen, N.P. (ed.). *Lepidoptera, moths and butterflies, volume 1, evolution, systematics, and biogeography*. Handbook of Zoology, Volume iv, part 35: 7–25. Walter de Gruyter. Berlin.

Kühne; G., KosuchL J., Hochkirch, A. & Schmitt, T. 2017. Extra-Mediterranean glacial refugia in a Mediterranean faunal element: the phylogeography of the chalkhill blue *Polyommatus coridon* (Lepidoptera, Lycaenidae). *Scientific Reports*. **7**: 43533; doi: 10.1038/srep43533.

Leather, S.R. 2009. Institutional vertebratism threatens UK food security. *Trends in Ecology & Evolution*. **24**: 413–414.

Leather, S.R. 2013. Institutional vertebratism hampers insect conservation generally; not just saproxylic beetle conservation. *Animal Conservation*. **16**: 379-380.

Leather, S.R. & Quicke, D.L.J. 2009. Where would Darwin have been without taxonomy? *Journal of Biological Education*. **43**: 51–52.

Leather, S.R. & Quicke, D.L.J. 2010. Do shifting baselines in natural history knowledge threaten the environment? *Environmentalist*. **30**: 1–2.

Lepertel, N. & Quinette, J.-P. 2016. *Atlas des papillons de nuit des basse-Normande et des îles Anglo-Normandes*. Normandy.

Lever, C. 1977. *The Naturalized Animals of the British Isles*. Hutchinson. London.

Lhomme, L. 1925. Une Noctuidae nouvelle decouverte en France, *Palluperina tardenota* de Joannis. *L'Amateur de Papillons*. **2**(16): 251–256.

Lhomme, L. 1926. *Palluperina tardenota* de Joannis (commentaire de la planche 5). *L'Amateur de Papillons*. **3**(10): 159–160.

Lockwood, R., Swaddle, J.P. & Rayner, J.M.V. 1998. Avian wingtip shape reconsidered: Wingtip shape indices and morphological adaptations to migration. *Journal of Avian Biology*. **29**(3): 273–292.

London, J. 1906. *White Fang*. Macmillan. New York.

Lövei, G.L. & Magura, T. 2017. Ground beetle (Coleoptera: Carabidae) diversity is higher in narrow hedges composed of a native compared to non-native trees in a Danish agricultural landscape. *Insect Conservation & Diversity*. **10**: 141–150.

Lundmark, C. 2010. Long-distance insect migration. *BioScience*. **60**(5): 400.

Mace, G.M. 2004. The role of taxonomy in species conservation. *Philosophical Transactions of the Royal Society of London B*. **359**: 711–719.

Mace, G.M. 2014. Whose conservation? *Science*. **345**: 1558–1560.

Macnair, M.R. 1987a. Heavy metal tolerance in plants: a model evolutionary system. *Trends in Ecology and Evolution*. **2**: 354–359.

Macnair, M.R. 1987b. Metal tolerance in mines in Devon: a natural evolutionary experiment. *Nature in Devon*. **8**: 29–44.

Maddison, D. & Day, B. 2014. *Improving Cost Benefit Analysis Guidance. A Report to the Natural Capital Committee*. NCC. Defra.

Mader, H.-J. 1984. Animal habitat isolation by roads and agricultural fields. *Biological Conservation*. **29**: 81–96.

Madge, S.C. 1999. The status of *Serapias parviflora* Parl. in Britain. *Botanical Cornwall*. **6**: 51–52.

Majerus, M.E.N. 1996. *Melanism. Evolution in Action*. Oxford University Press. Oxford.

Majerus, M.E.N. 2002. *Moths. The New Naturalist*. HarperCollins. London.

Marren, P. 2016. *Rainbow Dust: Three Centuries of Butterfly Delight*. Vintage Press. London.

Marren, P. & Warren, M. 2017. Britain's oldest butterfly – a "wonderful beautiful" survivor from Tudor England. *British Wildlife*. **28**: 323–325.

Martínková, N., McDonald, R.A. & Searle, J.B. 2007. Stoats (*Mustela erminea*) provide evidence of natural overland colonization of Ireland. *Proceedings of the Royal Society of London Series B*. **274**: 1387–1393.

McDevitt, A.D., Vega, R., Rambau, R.V., Yannic, G., Herman, J.S., Hayden, T.J. & Searle, J.B. 2011. Colonization of Ireland – revisiting 'the pygmy shrew syndrome' using mitochondrial, Y chromosomal and microsatellite markers. *Heredity*. **107**: 548–557.

Mcilveen, D. 2015. Argent & Sable *Rheumaptera hastata* (L., 1758) larva feeding on Himalyan Knotweed *Persicaria wallichii*. *Atropos*. **55**: 42–44.

Merrett, P. & Stevens, R.A.1995. A new genus and species of linyphiid spider from SW England. *Bulletin of the British Arachnological Society*. **10**(3): 118–120.

Mikkola, K. 2003. Red Admirals *Vanessa atalanta* (Lepidoptera: Nymphalidae) select northern winds on southward migration. *Entomologica Fennica*. **14**(1): 15–24. https://doi.org/10.33338/ef.84168.

Miller, N.G., Wassenaar, L.I., Hobson, K.A. & Norris, D.R. 2011. Monarch butterflies cross the Appalachians from the west to recolonize the east coast of North America. *Biology Letters*. **7**: 43-46.

Moffet, T. 1589. *Theatrum Insectorum*.

Monbiot, G. 2014. *Feral. Rewilding the Land, Sea and Human Life*. Penguin Books. London.

Morgan, D. 2019. Long-distance dispersal and establishment by orchids. *British Wildlife*. **30**: 344–351.

Moroń, D., Grześ, I., Skórka, P., Szentgyörgyi, H., Laskowski, R., Potts, S. & Woyciechowski, M. 2012. Abundance and diversity of wild bees along gradients of heavy metal pollution. *Journal of Applied Ecology*. **49**: 118–125. 10.1111/j.1365-2664.2011.02079.x.

Morris, M.G., Thomas, J.A., Ward, L.K., Snazell, R.G., Pywell, R.F., Stevenson, M.J. & Webb, N.R. 1994. Recreation of early successional stages for threatened butterflies – an ecological engineering approach. *Journal of Environmental Management*. **42**: 119–135.

Mouritsen, H., Heyers, D. & Güntürkün, O. 2016. The neural basis of long-distance navigation in birds. *Annual Review of Physiology.* **78**: 133–154. doi: 10. 1146/annurev-physiol-021115-105054.

Munguira, M.L. & Thomas, J.A. 1992. Use of road verges by butterfly and burnet populations, and the effect of roads on adult dispersal. *Journal of Applied Ecology.* **29**: 316–329.

Nakatani T., Usami S. & Itoh T. 2007. Phylogenetic history of the Japanese Alpine ringlet *Erebia niphonica* (Lepidoptera, Nymphalidae): Fragmentation and secondary contact. *Transactions of the Lepidopterological Society of Japan.* **58**: 253–275.

Nawroth, C., Brett, J.M. & McElligott, A.G. 2016. Goats display audience-dependent human-directed gazing behaviour in a problem-solving task. *Biology Letters.* **12**: 20160283. http://dx.doi.org/10.1098/rsbl.2016.0283.

Nazari, V., Tarmann, G.M. & Efetov, K.A. 2019. Phylogenetic position of the 'extinct' Fijian coconut moth, *Levuana iridescens* (Lepidoptera: Zygaenidae). *PLOS One.* **14**(12): e0225590. https://doi.org/10.1371/journal.pone.0225590.

Nève, G. 2009. Population genetics of butterflies. In: J. Settle, T. Shreeve, M. Konvička & H. Van Dyck. (eds.). *Ecology of Butterflies in Europe.* Cambridge University Press. Cambridge.

Nowinszky L. 2003. The orientation of insects by light—major theories. In: *The handbook of light trapping.* Savaria University Press. Szombathely (Hungary). pp. 15–18.

Oakes, L. 2011. Notes on the occurrence of *Barea asbolaea* (Meyr.) in Cornwall. *Atropos.* **44**: 33–36.

Oates. M. 2020. *His Imperial Majesty. A natural history of the Purple Emperor.* Bloomsbury Wildlife. London.

Oates, M.R. & Warren, M.S. 1990. *A review of butterfly introductions in Britain and Ireland.* World Wildlife Fund.

O'Meara, D.B., Edwards, C.J. Sleeman, D.P., Cross, T.F., Statham, M.J., Mcdowell, J.R., Dillane, E., Coughlan, J.P., O'Leary, D., O'Reilly, C., Bradley, D.G. & Carlsson, J. 2012. Genetic structure of Eurasian badgers *Meles meles* (Carnivora: Mustelidae) and the colonization history of Ireland. *Biological Journal of the Linnean Society.* **106**: 893–909.

Owen, D. 1985. *What's in a name. A look at the origins of plant and animal names.* BBC. London.

Owens, A.C.S. & Lewis, S.M. 2018. The impact of artificial light at night on nocturnal insects: A review and synthesis. *Ecology and Evolution.* **8**: 11337–11358. DOI: 10.1002/ece3.4557.

Parsons, M., Wainwright, C., Hetherington, H. & Wheeler, K. 2016. *Cornifrons ulceratalis* Lederer, 1858 – A crambid new to the British Isles. *Atropos.* **56**: 32–43.

Pedersen, N.C., Pooch, A.S. & Liu, H. 2016. A genetic assessment of the English bulldog. *Canine Genetics and Epidemiology.* **3**(6): https://doi.org/10.1186/s40575-016-0036-y.

Pellow, K. 1999. An influx of Green Darner *Anax junius* (Drury) into Cornwall and the Isles of Scilly – The First European Records. *Atropos.* **6**: 3–7.

Penney, D. 2016. *Amber Palaeobiology: research trends and perspectives for the 21st century*. Siri Scientific Press. Manchester.

Pennisi, E. 2019. DNA barcodes jump-start search for new species. *Science*. **364** (6444): 920–921.

Peterken, G. 2019. Defining "natural woodland." *British Wildlife*. **30**(3): 157–159.

Petiver, J. 1695. *Musei Petiverani Centuria prima rariora Naturae*. London.

Pfenninger, M. & Schwenk, K. 2007. Cryptic animal species are homogeneously distributed among taxa and biogeographical regions. *BMC Evolutionary Biology*. **7**: 121. https://doi.org/10.1186/1471-2148-7-121.

Plant, C.W., Poole, C., Salisbury A. & Bird, S. 2019. The Box-tree Moth *Cydalima perspectalis* (Walker, 1859) in Britain: an overview of its spread and current status. *The Entomologist's Record and Journal of Variation*. **131**: 122–147.

Port, G.R. & Thompson, J.R. 1980. Outbreaks of insect herbivores on plants along motorways in the United Kingdom. *Journal of Applied Ecology*. **17**: 649–656.

Pratt, C.R. 2020. *A Revised History of the Butterflies and Moths of Sussex*. Volume 4. Pratt. Sussex.

Prescott, T. 2017. Getting to grips with the Pine-tree Lappet. Conservation and Research News. *Butterfly*. **125**: 26–27.

Presly, F. 2018. Observations of a wingless Bumblebee Queen. *Antenna*. **42**(1): 3-4.

Preston, C.D., Pearman, D.A. & Dines, T.D. 2002. *New Atlas of the British and Irish Flora: An Atlas of the Vascular Plants of Britain, Ireland, The Isle of Man and the Channel Islands*. Oxford University Press. Oxford.

Pyle, R.M. 2010. Under their own steam: the biogeographic case against butterfly releases. *News of the Lepidopterists' Society*. **52**(2): 54–57.

Rackham, O. 2019. *The Ancient Woods of the Helford River*. Little Toller Books. Dorset.

Ratcliffe, D. 1977. *A Nature Conservation Review*. Cambridge University Press. Cambridge.

Ravenscroft, N.O.M. & Young, M.R. 1996. Habitat specificity, restricted range and metapopulation persistence of the Slender Scotch Burnet Moth *Zygaena loti* in western Scotland. *Journal of Applied Ecology*. **33**(5): 993–1000.

Ray, J. 1710. *Historia Insectorum*. (published posthumously).

Reid, N. 2018. The Irish Hare: from the ice age to the present. *British Wildlife*. **29**: 237–243.

Reppert, S.M., Gegear, R.J. & Merlin, C. 2010. Navigational mechanisms of migrating monarch butterflies. *Trends in neurosciences*. **33**(9): 399–406.

Reynolds, A.M., Reynolds, D.R., Sane, S.P., Hu, G. & Chapman, J.W. 2016. Orientation in high-flying migrant insects in relation to flows: mechanisms and strategies. *Philosophical Transactions of the Royal Society of London B*. https://doi.org/10.1098/rstb.2015.0392.

Reynolds, S. 2019. A trick of the light? Artificial light at night, insects and spiders. *Antenna*. **43**(4): 159–163.

Riddiford, N.J. & Young, M.R. 2017. The Moths and Butterflies (Lepidoptera) of Fair Isle. *Entomologist's Gazette*. **68**: 275–308.

Robertson, J. 2016. A study in pink. *British Wildlife*. **27**: 154–160.

Robinson, H.S. & Robinson, P.J.M. 1950. Some notes on the observed behaviour of

Lepidoptera in flight in the vicinity of light-sources together with a description of a light trap designed to take entomological samples. *Entomologist's Gazette.* **11**: 121–132.

Roca, A.L., Georgiadis, N., Pecon-Slattery, J. & O'Brien, S.J. 2001. Genetic evidence for two species of elephant in Africa. *Science.* **293**: 1473–1477.

Roosevelt, T. 1909–1910. *African Game Trails. An Account of the Wanderings of an American Hunter-Naturalist.* C. Scribner's Magazine. New York.

Rose, B. 2017. The spread of Turkey Oak in the British Isles. *British Wildlife.* **28**: 176–185.

Rotherham, I.D. 2014. The Call of the Wild – Perceptions, history, people and ecology in the emerging paradigms of wilding. *Ecos.* **35**(1): 1–17.

Rothschild, M. 1991. *Butterfly cooing like a Dove.* Doubleday. London.

Rousselet, J., Zhao, R., Argal, D., Simonato, M., Battisti, A., Roques, A. & Kerdelhué, C. 2010. The role of topography in structuring the demographic history of the pine processionary moth, *Thaumetopoea pityocampa* (Lepidoptera: Notodontidae). *Journal of Biogeography.* **37**: 1478–1490. doi:10.1111/j.1365-2699.2010.02289.x.

Rule, A. & Levine, D. 2012. International Art English: On the rise, and the space, of the art world press release. *Triple Canopy.* **16**: 7–30.

Ruskin, J. 1856. *Modern Painters. Volume III.* National Library Association. New York.

Russell, J.C. 2012. Do invasive species cause damage. Yes? *Bioscience.* **62**(3): 217.

Rydell, J. & Lancaster, W.C. 2000. Flight and thermoregulation in moths were shaped by predation from bats. *Oikos.* **88**:13–18.

Salmon, M.A. 2000. *The Aurelian Legacy. British butterflies and their collectors* (with additional material by P. Marren & B. Harley). Harley Books. Colchester.

Salway, K. 1996. *Collectors Items.* Wilderness Editions.

Sanson, C.J. 2006. *Winter in Madrid.* Pan Books. London.

Sartre, J.-P. 1938. *Nausea.* Penguin Books.

Sartre, J.-P. 1945. *L'existentialisme est un humanisme Lecture.* Paris. (29th October 1945).

Schmitt, T. 2009. Biogeographical and evolutionary importance of the European high mountain systems. *Frontiers in Zoology.* doi:10.1186/1742-9994-6-9.

Schmitt, T. & Hewitt, G.M. 2004. Molecular biogeography of the arctic-alpine disjunct burnet moth species *Zygaena exulans* (Zygaenidae, Lepidoptera) in the Pyrenees and Alps. *Journal of Biogeography.* **31**: 885–893. doi:10.1111/j.1365-2699.2004.01079.x.

Schmitt, T., Hewitt, G.M. & Müller, P. 2006. Disjunct distributions during glacial and interglacial periods in mountain butterflies: *Erebia epiphron* as an example. *Journal of Evolutionary Biology.* **19**: 108–113 doi: 10.1111/j.1420-9101.2005.00980.

Schmitt, T., Röber, S. & Seitz, A. 2005. Is the last glaciation the only relevant event for the present genetic population structure of the meadow brown butterfly *Maniola jurtina* (Lepidoptera: Nymphalidae)? *Biological Journal of the Linnean Society.* **85**: 419–431.

Schmitt, T. & Seitz, A. 2001. Intraspecific allozymatic differentiation reveals the glacial refugia and the postglacial expansions of European *Erebia medusa* (Lepidoptera: Nymphalidae). *Biological Journal of the Linnean Society.* **74**: 429–458.

Schmitt, T. & Varga, Z. 2012. Extra-Mediterranean refugia: The rule and not the exception? *Frontiers in Zoology.* DOI: 10.1186/1742-9994-9-22.

Scoble, M.J. 2002. *The Lepidoptera: Form, Function and Diversity.* Oxford University Press. Oxford.

Scott, J.A. 1973. Population biology and adult behaviour of the circumpolar butterfly *Parnassius phoebus* F. (Papilionidae). *Entomologica Scandinavica.* **4**: 161–168.

Scruton, R. 1996. *Animal Rights and Wrongs.* Demos. London.

Shamoun-Baranes, J., Nilsson, C., Bauer, S. & Chapman, J. 2019. Taking radar aeroecology into the 21st century. *Ecography.* **42**: 847–851 doi: 10.1111/ecog.04582.

Shannon, L.M., Boyko, R.H., Castelhano, M., Corey, E., Hayward, J.J., McLean, C., White, M.E., Abi Said, M., Anita, B.A., Bondjengo, N.I., Calero, J., Galov, A., Hedimbi, M., Imam, B., Khalap, R., Lally, D., Masta, A., Oliveira, K.C., Pérez, L., Randall, J., Tam, N.M., Trujillo-Cornejo, F.J., Valeriano, C., Sutter, N.B., Todhunter, R.J., Bustamante, C.D. & Boyko, A.R. 2015. Genetic structure in village dogs reveals a Central Asian domestication origin. *Proceedings of the National Academy of Science.* **112**(44): 13639–13644. doi: 10.1073/pnas.1516215112. Epub 2015 Oct 19. PMID: 26483491; PMCID: PMC4640804.

Sharkey, M.J., Janzen, D.H., Hallwachs, W., Chapman, E.G., Smith, M.A., Dapkey, T., Brown, A., Ratnasingham, S., Naik, S., Manjunath, R., Perez, K., Milton, M., Hebert, P., Shaw, S.R., Kittel, R.N., Solis, M.A., Metz, M.A., Goldstein, P.Z., Brown, J.W., Quicke, D.L.J., van Achterberg, C., Brown, B.V. & Burns J.M. 2021. Minimalist revision and description of 403 new species in 11 subfamilies of Costa Rican braconid parasitoid wasps, including host records for 219 species. *ZooKeys.* **1013**: 1–665.

Signorile, A.L., Reuman, D.C., Lurz, P.W.W., Bertolino, S., Carbone, C. & Wang, J. 2016. Using DNA profiling to investigate human-mediated translocations of an invasive species. *Biological Conservation.* **195**: 97–105.

Sivinski, J. 1981. Arthropods attracted to luminous fungi. *Psyche.* **88**: 383–390.

Snell, C. 2016. The Northern Pool Frog – research, reintroduction and range. *British Wildlife.* **28**: 2–11.

Snell, C., Tetteh, J. & Evans, I.H. 2005. Phylogeography of the pool frog (*Rana lessonae* Camerano) in Europe: evidence for native status in Great Britain and for an unusual postglacial colonization route. *Biological Journal of the Linnean Society.* **85**: 41–51.

Soga, M. & Gaston, K.J. 2020. The ecology of human – nature interactions. *Proceedings of the Royal Society B.* 287. 20191882. http://dx.doi.org/10.1098/rspb.2019.1882.

Sohn, J., Labandeira, C., Davis, D. & Mitter, C. 2012. An annotated catalog of fossil and subfossil Lepidoptera (Insecta: Holometabola) of the world. *Zootaxa.* ps://doi.org/10.11646/zootaxa.3286.1.

Sommer, R.S. & Zachos, F.E. 2009. Fossil evidence and phylogeography of temperate species: 'glacial refugia' and post-glacial recolonization. *Journal of Biogeography.* **36**: 2013–2020.

Sotthibandhu, S. & Baker, R.R. 1979. Celestial orientation by the large yellow underwing moth, *Noctua pronuba* L. *Animal Behaviour.* **27**: 786–800.

Southwood, T.R.E. 1961. The number of species of insect associated with various trees. *Journal of Animal Ecology.* **30**: 1–8.

Spalding, A. 1988. The moths of Wistman's Wood, Dartmoor. *British Journal of Entomology and Natural History.* **1**(4): 129–132.

Spalding, A. 1996. The importance of metalliferous mining sites in Cornwall for wildlife, with special reference to the insects. *Cornish Studies (Second Series).* **3**: 161–175.

Spalding, A. 1997. The use of the butterfly transect method for the study of the nocturnal moth *Luperina nickerlii leechi* Goater (Lepidoptera: Noctuidae) and its possible application to other species. *Biological Conservation.* **80**: 147–152.

Spalding, A. 2003. Species Profile: Scarce Blackneck *Lygephila craccae* (D.& S.). *Atropos.* **19**: 29–33.

Spalding, A. 2005. *The Butterfly Handbook. General advice note on mitigating the impacts of roads on butterfly populations.* English Nature & Highways Agency.

Spalding, A. 2009. The Silver-studded Blue *Plebejus argus* (Linn.): Staying true to its foodplant. *Atropos.* **38**: 14–18.

Spalding, A. 2013. The morphometrics of *Luperina nickerlii* (Freyer) (Lepidoptera: Noctuidae) in Europe; wing measurements and body length in the different subspecies. *Entomologist's Gazette.* **64**: 135–144.

Spalding, A. 2015. *Loe Bar and the Sandhill Rustic Moth. The Biogeography, Ecology and Cultural History of a Coastal Shingle Bar.* Brill Academic Publishing. Leiden.

Spalding, A. 2019. Light pollution and the decline of moths. Presidential Address. *British Journal of Entomology and Natural History.* **32**: 17–34.

Spalding, A., Collins, G.A. & Haes, E.C.M. 2008. Factors affecting the presence of insects on a small un-vegetated bank at an abandoned mining site in west Cornwall. *British Journal of Entomology and Natural History.* **21**: 205–214.

Spalding, A & Dinsdale, J. 2000. Derelict metalliferous sites: the case for conservation. In: Fox, H.R. & Moore, H.M. *Land Reclamation and Regeneration, the Proceedings of the British Land Reclamation Society and National Land Reclamation Panel Conference.* Camborne School of Mines.

Spalding, A. & Haes, E.C.M. 1995. Contaminated Land – A resource for wildlife: a review and survey of insects on metalliferous mine sites in Cornwall. *Land Contamination and Reclamation.* **3**: 24–29.

Spalding, A., Hartgroves, S., Macadam, J. & Owens, D. (eds). 2002. *The conservation value of abandoned pits and quarries in Cornwall.* Cornwall Archaeological Unit, Cornwall County Council. Truro.

Spalding, A. & Jenkin, L.E.T. 1988. Cornish names for moths. *Entomologist's*

Record and Journal of Variation. **100**: 253–254.

Spalding, A. & Parsons, M. 2004. Light trap transects – a field method for ascertaining the habitat preferences of night-flying Lepidoptera, using *Mythima turca* (Linnaeus 1761) (Lepidoptera: Noctuidae) as an example. *Journal of Insect Conservation*. **8**: 185–190.

Spalding, A., Shanks, K., Bennie J., Potter, U.J. & ffrench-Constant, R.F. 2019. Optical modelling and phylogenetic analysis provide clues to the likely function of corneal nipple arrays in butterflies and moths including the reason why moths come to UV light. *Insects*. **10**: 262; doi:10.3390/insects10090262.

Spalding Associates (Environmental) Ltd. 2001. *Skylark Surveys at Penhale Dunes, Perranporth, Cornwall*. Truro.

Spalding, A., Tunmore, M., Parsons, M. & Fox, R. 2005. The state of moth recording in Britain: The results of the National Macro-moth Recording Scheme Consultation Questionnaire. *Atropos*. **24**: 9–19.

Spalding, J. 2016. Introduction to Measures, D. 216. *Kaleidoscope: The Secret Lives of Britain's Butterflies*. Mascot Media. Norwich.

Sparks, T.H., Roy, D.B. & Dennis, R.L.H. 2005. The influence of temperature on migration of Lepidoptera into Britain. *Global Change Biology*. **11**: 507–514.

Sproul, J. 2015. Elephant hawk-moth *Deilephila elpenor* feeding upon Himalayan Balsam *Impatiens glandulifera*. *Atropos*. **55**: 61–62.

Stace, C.A. & Crawley, M.J. 2015. *Alien Plants*. The New Naturalist Library. HarperCollins. London.

Stefanescu, C., Alarcón, M. & Àvila, A. 2007. Migration of the Painted Lady butterfly, *Vanessa cardui*, to north-eastern Spain is aided by African wind currents. *Journal of Animal Ecology*. **76**: 888–898.

Stefanescu, C., Soto, D.X., Talavera, G., Vila, R. & Hobson, K.A. 2016. Long-distance autumn migration across the Sahara by Painted Lady butterflies: exploiting resource pulses in the tropical savannah. *Biology Letters*. https://doi.org/10.1098/rsbl.2016.0561.

Sterling, P. & Parsons, M. 2012. *Field Guide to the Micro-moths of Great Britain and Ireland*. British Wildlife Publishing. Gilllingham.

Strachan, R. & Moorhouse, T. 2006. *Water Vole Conservation Handbook*. Wildlife Conservation Research Unit. Tubney.

Strickland, P. 2019. Irish China-Mark *Elophila rivulalis* (Duponchel, 1834): new to Britain and Ireland. *Atropos*. **63**: 31–35.

Sturt, F., Garrow, D. & Bradley, S. 2013. New models of North West European Holocene palaeogeography and inundation. *Journal of Archaeological Science*. **40**: 3963–3976.

Sumner, S., Law, G. & Cini, A. 2018. Why we love bees and wasps. *Ecological Entomology*. **43**: 836–845.

Taylor, R.A.J. 1986. Time series analysis of numbers of Lepidoptera caught at light traps in East Africa, and the effect of moonlight on trap efficiency. *Bulletin of Entomological Research*. **76**(4): 593–606.

The British Hedgehog Preservation Society & the People's Trust for Endangered Species. 2018. *The State of Britain's Hedgehogs*.

Thomas, C.D. 2017. *Inheritors of the Earth. How Nature is Thriving in an Age of Extinction*. Allen Lane. London.

Thomas, C.D., Glen, S.W.T., Lewis, O.T., Hill, J.K. & Blakeley, D.S. 1999. Population differentiation and conservation of endemic races: the butterfly, *Plebejus argus*. *Animal Conservation*. **2**: 15–21.

Thomas, C.D., Thomas, J.A. & Warren, M.S. 1992. Distribution of occupied and vacant butterfly habitats in fragmented landscapes. *Oecologia*. **92**: 563–567.

Thomas, J.A., Snazell, R.G. & Ward, L.K. 2002. Are roads harmful or potentially beneficial to butterflies and other insects? In: Sherwood, B., Cutler, D. & Burton, J.A. *Wildlife and Roads. The Ecological Impact*. Imperial College Press. London.

Thompson, K. 2015. *Where do Camels belong? The story and Science of Invasive Species*. Profile Books. London.

Tilley, R.J.D. & Dennis, R.L.H. 2017. Assessing probabilities of island location and occupation: a butterfly individual's perspective. *Entomologist's Gazette*. **68**: 161–175.

Tison, J-L., Edmark, V.N., Sandoval-Castellanos, E., Van Dyck, H., Tammaru, T., Välimäki, P., Dalén, L. & Gotthard, K. 2014. Signature of post-glacial expansion and genetic structure at the northern range limit of the speckled wood butterfly. *Biological Journal of the Linnean Society*. **113**: 136–148.

Torniainen, J. & Mikonranta, L. 2018. The origins of northern European *Autographa gamma* individuals evaluated using hydrogen stable isotopes. *Ecological Entomology*. **43**: 699–702.

Troscianko J. & Rutz C. 2015. Activity profiles and hook-tool use of New Caledonian crows recorded by bird-borne video cameras. *Biology Letters*. **11**: 20150777. http://dx.doi.org/10.1098/rsbl.2015.0777.

Trouwborst, A., Krofel, M & Linnell, J.D.C. 2015. Legal implications of range expansions in a terrestrial carnivore: the case of the golden jackal (*Canis aureus*) in Europe. *Biodiversity Conservation*. **24**: 2593–2610. DOI 10.1007/s10531-015-0948-y.

Tuf, I.H., Drábková, L. & Šipoš, J. 2015. Personality affects defensive behaviour of *Porcellio scaber* (Isopoda, Oniscidea). *Zookeys*. **515**: 159–171.

Tunmore, M. 2015. The first British record of Boathouse Gem (Boisd., 1840). *Atropos*. **55**: 3–13.

Turpin, M.A., Walker, A.C., Kara-Yakoubian, M., Gabert, N.N., Fugelsang, J.A. & Stolz, J.A. 2019. Bullshit makes the art grow profounder. *Judgment and Decision Making*. **14**(6): 658–670.

Tyler, J. 1994. *Glow-worms*. Tyler-Scagell. Stratford.

Tyson, M. 2013. *The Undisputed Truth. An Autobiography*. HarperSport.

Ulrich, W., Bąkowski, A. & Laštǔvka, Z. 2011. Spatial distributions of European clearwing moths (Lepidoptera: Sesiidae). *European Journal of Entomology*. **108**: 439–446.

Ursenbacher, S., Guillon, M., Cubizolle, H., Dupoué, A., Blouin-Demers, G. & Lourdais, O. 2015. Postglacial recolonization in a cold climate specialist in western Europe: patterns of genetic diversity in the adder (*Vipera berus*) support the central-marginal hypothesis. *Molecular Ecology*. **24**(14): 3639-51. doi: 10.1111/mec.13259.

Vandevelde, J., Penone, C. & Julliard, R. 2012. High-speed railways are not barriers to *Pyronia tithonus* butterfly movements. *Journal of Insect Conservation*. **16**: 801–803. https://doi.org/10.1007/s10841-012-9513-0.

Vane-Wright, R.I., Fage, J. & Huertas, B. 2017. The Brighton Monarch 2015 – born free, or escapee? *Entomologist's Gazette*. **68**: 73–84.

Van Langevelde, F., Ettema, J.A., Donners, M., Wallis DeVries, M.F. & Groenendijk, D. 2011. Effect of spectral composition of artificial light on the attraction of moths. *Biological Conservation*. **144**: 2274–2281.

Vickers, N.J. & Baker, T.C. 1994. Visual feedback in the control of pheromone-mediated flight of *Heliothis virescens* males (Lepidoptera: Noctuidae). *Journal of Insect Behaviour*. **7**: 605–632.

Vo Doan, T.T. & Sato, H. 2016. Insect-machine hybrid system: Remote radio control of a freely flying beetle (*Mercynorrhina torquata*). *Journal of Visualised Experiments*. **115**, e54260, doi:10.3791/54260.

Wallace, A.R. 1869. *The Malay Archipelago. The land of the Orang-utan and the Bird of Paradise. A narrative of travel with the studies of man and nature.* Macmillan & Co. Last revised (10th) edition. Tynron Press. Thornhill.

Waring, P. & Townsend, M. 2003. *Field Guide to the Moths of Great Britain and Ireland*. British Wildlife Publishing. Hook.

Warrant, E., Frost, B., Green, K., Mouritsen, H., Dreyer, D., Adden, A., Brauburger, K. & Heinze, S. 2016. The Australian Bogong Moth *Agrotis infusa*: A long-distance nocturnal navigator. *Frontiers in Behavioral Neuroscience*. **10**: 77. doi: 10.3389/fnbeh.2016.00077.

Way, J.M. 1977. Roadside verges and conservation in Britain: a review. *Biological Conservation*. **12**: 65–74.

Webb, D.A. 1985. What are the criteria for presuming native status? *Watsonia*. **15**: 231–236.

Weissbrod, L., Marshall, F.B., Valla, F.R., Khalaily, H., Bar-Oz, G., Auffray, J-C., Vigne, J-D. & Cucchi, T. 2017. Origins of house mice in ecological niches created by settled hunter-gatherers in the Levant 15,000 y ago. *Proceedings of the National Academy of Sciences*. https://doi.org/10.1073/pnas.1619137114.

Weninger, B., Schulting, R., Bradtmoller, M., Clare, L., Collard, M., Edinborough, K., Hilpert, J., Joris, O., Niekus, M., Rohiling, E.J. & Wagner, B. 2008. The catastrophic final flooding of Doggerland by the Storegga Slide tsunami. *Documenta Praehistorica*. XXXV, 1e24.

Whalley, P.E.S. 1985. The systematics and palaeogeography of the Lower Jurassic insects of Dorset, England. *Bulletin British Museum Natural History, Geology*. **39**: 107–189.

Whitbread-Abrutat, P.H. 1995. *The improvement of tree establishment on metalliferous mine wastes. PhD thesis.* Camborne School of Mines. University of Exeter.

Whitehead, P.F. 1996. *Eucnemis capucina* Ahrens 1812 (Col., Eucnemidae) at three sites in Worcestershire with a remarkable beetle fauna on *Quercus cerris* L. at one site. *Entomologist's Monthly Magazine*. **132**: 187–195.

Whiting, S.N., Reeves, R.D. & Baker, A.J.M. 2002. Conserving biodiversity. Mining, metallophytes and land reclamation. *Mining Environmental Management*. **10**: 11–16.

Wickman, P.-O. 1992. Sexual selection and butterfly design – a comparative study. *Evolution*. **46**: 1525–1536. doi: 10.1111/j.1558-5646.1992.tb01142.x.

Wilkes, B. 1747–1749. *The English Moths and Butterflies, together with the plants, flowers and fruits whereon which they feed, and are usually found*. Fleet Street. London.

Williams, W.D. & Busby, J.R. 1991. The geographical distribution of *Triops australiensis* (Crustacea: Notostraca) in Australia: a biogeoclimatic analysis. *Hydrobiologia*. **212**: 235–240. https://doi.org/10.1007/BF00026006.

Wilson, E. 1992. *The diversity of life*. Harvard University Press. Cambridge MA.

Wilson R.A. & Barker, M.J. 2013. The biological notion of individual. In: *Stanford Encyclopedia of Philosophy*. http://plato.stanford.edu/entries/biology-individual/.

Witter, E., Giller, K.E. & McGrath, S.P. 1994. Long term effects of metal contamination on soil micro-organisms. *Soil Biology and Biochemistry*. **26**: 421–422.

Wulf, A. 2015. *The Invention of Nature. The Adventures of Alexander Humbold, the Lost Hero of Science*. John Murray. London.

Young, M. 1997. *The Natural History of Moths*. Poyser Natural History. London.

Zakharov, B.P. 2013. *Nomosystematics: A Closer Look at the Theoretical Foundation of Biological Classification*. Siri Scientific Press. Manchester.

APPENDIX: What are species?

Throughout this book I have discussed issues relating to the diverse practical elements of our wildlife that may easily be overlooked or unappreciated when considering or formulating conservation plans. I have used many different species as examples – some will be familiar to most readers whereas others will not. But how do we fare on the theoretical side of things? Can we even define what a species truly is?

There is a long-established and generally accepted definition (for extant organisms) which many people accept without question: "A group of living organisms consisting of similar individuals capable of exchanging genes or interbreeding to produce fertile offspring." However, can we really shoehorn the immense vastness of biological diversity into this rather simplistic definition and the human-derived taxonomic constructs, axiomatically limited by our own imagination and ability to define such things? As humans, we strive for orderliness and systems to explain and classify natural phenomena, but the mega-diversity of the natural world has no 'need nor desire' to conform to any such unnatural constructs, which attempt to pose order on it (e.g. Zakharov 2013).

There is ongoing debate among scientists as to how we define species and understand how they are related to one another. After a long period of relative stasis, the past few decades have seen great changes in how we approach these topics and this continues apace. The advent of computer-based cladistic methods and molecular phylogenetic techniques have demonstrated some new relationships to those traditionally accepted based on standard morphological investigation and have settled many long-standing controversies (Kjer *et al.* 2016). They have even identified surprising examples of cryptic species that have been wandering around in plain sight right in front of us. For example, the African Elephant is now known to represent two distinct but cryptic species, which are incapable of interbreeding: The African Elephant and the African Bush Elephant (Roca *et al.* 2001). More recently, due to advances in next generation sequencing, new species have begun to be described and diagnosed solely on the basis of a genetic barcode (Pennisi 2019; Sharkey *et al.* 2021). This has stimulated heated debate, with some taxonomists accepting that this is the way forwards and that eventually all species will be redefined and classified in this way, but with others predicting utter chaos. Indeed, progress in this area is the only way that further cryptic species complexes will be discovered and these are now thought to be much more widespread than previously accepted – and may only be separated by reproductive behaviour - which has direct theoretical and practical consequences for a number of prevailing biological questions with regard to global biodiversity estimates and conservation efforts (Pfenninger & Schwenk 2007). These studies emphasise again that wildlife does not conform to our compulsion to shoehorn everything into our systematic approach.

GENERAL INDEX

SPECIES INDEX

153

Vascular Plants

North American Beaver *Castor canadensis* 18, 85, 86, 118
Otter *Lutra lutra* 70
Pygmy Shrew *Sorex minutus* 37
Rabbit *Oryctolagus cuniculus* 43, 57, 72, 108
Red Deer *Cervus elaphus* 34, 66, 70, 118
Red Fox *Vulpes vulpes* 24, 107, 118
Red Panda *Ailurus fulgens* 19
Roe Deer *Capreolus capreolus* 34, 118
Scilly Shrew (Lesser White-toothed Shrew) *Crocidura suaveolens* 31, 79
Scimitar-toothed Cat *Homotherium latidens* 34
Short-tailed Mouse *Mus macedonicus* 67, 68
Siberian Chipmunks *Tamias sibiricus* 75
Snow Leopard *Panthera uncia* 15, 19, 20
Sperm Whale *Physeter macrocephalus* 60
Spotted Hyena *Crocuta crocuta* 86
Straight-Tusked Elephant *Palaeoloxodon antiquus* 86
Warthog *Phacochoerus africanus* 19
Water Vole *Arvicola amphibius* 38, 70
White Rhinocerus *Ceratotherium simum* 19
Wild Boar *Sus scrofa* 71, 84, 86, 118
Wild Camel *Camelus ferus* 35
Woolly Mammoth *Mammuthus primigenius* 34, 87
Woolly Rhino *Coelodonta antiquitatis* 34, 87

Birds
Cirl Bunting *Emberiza cirlus* 82
Common Crane *Grus grus* 85, 86
Dodo *Raphus cucullatus* 29
Grey Catbird *Dumetella carolinensis* 89
Manx Shearwater *Puffinus puffinus* 79
New Caledonian Crow *Corvus moneduloides* 25
Pale-browed Tinamou *Crypturellus transfasciatus* 33
Peregrine Falcon *Falco peregrinus* 104, 107
Pheasant *Phasianus colchius* 54, 72
Red-legged Partridge *Alectoris rufa* 74
Red-tailed Hawk *Buteo jamaicensis* 75
Robin *Erithacus rubecula* 92
Skylark *Alauda arvensis* 65, 108, 118
Storm Petrel *Hydrobates pelagicus* 79
White-tailed Sea Eagle *Haliaeetus albicilla* 85, 86
Wilson's Warbler *Cardellina pusilla* 88, 102
Zebra Finch *Taeniopygia guttata* 119

Others
Common Octopus *Octopus vulgaris* 24, 25
Grass Carp *Ctenophary idella* 72

About the author

Adrian Spalding has run an environmental consultancy for over 20 years and has worked with wildlife charities, statutory authorities, council planners, developers, highways agencies, railway companies and renewable energy companies throughout the UK. He has travelled widely in six of the seven continents. He is an Honorary Research Fellow at the University of Exeter, a member of the Conservation Committee of the Royal Entomological Society, editor of the *Entomologist's Gazette*, former President of the British Entomological and Natural History Society, former Academic Director, Cornish Biological Records Unit (University of Exeter) and past member of the Council of Butterfly Conservation. A qualified teacher, he also has degrees in history and zoology. He used to host a weekly wildlife programme on Radio Cornwall. He has written several books on wildlife and won the Holyer an Gof prize for his book *Loe Bar and the Sandhill Rustic Moth*. His interest in butterflies and moths dates back to when he was eight-years-old, watching an Indian Moon Moth emerge from its cocoon and expand its long tails on the living room window sill; the moth Spalding's Dart is named after him.